yourself

tantric sex
richard craze

For over 60 years, more than
50 million people have learnt over
750 subjects the **teach yourself**
way, with impressive results.

be where you want to be
with **teach yourself**

For UK order enquiries: please contact Bookpoint Ltd, 130 Milton Park, Abingdon, Oxon, OX14 4SB. Telephone: +44 (0) 1235 827720. Fax: +44 (0) 1235 400454. Lines are open 09.00–17.00, Monday to Saturday, with a 24-hour message answering service. Details about our titles and how to order are available at www.teachyourself.co.uk

For USA order enquiries: please contact McGraw-Hill Customer Services, PO Box 545, Blacklick, OH 43004-0545, USA. Telephone: 1-800-722-4726. Fax: 1-614-755-5645.

For Canada order enquiries: please contact McGraw-Hill Ryerson Ltd, 300 Water St, Whitby, Ontario, L1N 9B6, Canada. Telephone: 905 430 5000. Fax: 905 430 5020.

Long renowned as the authoritative source for self-guided learning – with more than 50 million copies sold worldwide – the **teach yourself** series includes over 500 titles in the fields of languages, crafts, hobbies, business, computing and education.

British Library Cataloguing in Publication Data: a catalogue record for this title is available from the British Library.

Library of Congress Catalog Card Number: on file.

First published in UK 2002 by Hodder Education, 338 Euston Road, London, NW1 3BH.

First published in US 2002 by The McGraw-Hill Companies, Inc.

This edition published 2007; updated with two additional chapters by Paul Jenner

The **teach yourself** name is a registered trade mark of Hodder Headline.

Copyright © 2002, 2003, 2007 Richard Craze and Paul Jenner

Typeset by Transet Limited, Coventry, England.
Printed in Great Britain for Hodder Education, a division of Hodder Headline, 338 Euston Road, London, NW1 3BH, by Cox & Wyman Ltd, Reading, Berkshire.

The publisher has used its best endeavours to ensure that the URLs for external websites referred to in this book are correct and active at the time of going to press. However, the publisher and the author have no responsibility for the websites and can make no guarantee that a site will remain live or that the content will remain relevant, decent or appropriate.

Hodder Headline's policy is to use papers that are natural, renewable and recyclable products and made from wood grown in sustainable forests. The logging and manufacturing processes are expected to conform to the environmental regulations of the country of origin.

Impression number   10 9 8 7 6 5 4 3 2 1
Year   2010 2009 2008 2007

contents

This book has been updated by Paul Jenner, who has added two new chapters.

This book is dedicated to Sarah Wood whose knowledge of tantra has always been such an inspiration to us all.

01

what this book is about

In this chapter you will learn:
- about spirituality and sexuality
- a new approach to sexuality
- the fundamental aims of tantric sex.

Do the caress for your own pleasure. Focus on exactly what you are feeling. Notice how concentrating on your own sensations makes you much more attentive to the little things: the little warm spots, the places where the skin is most delicate, the areas of extreme sensitivity. How does it all feel against your tongue?

Barbara Keesling, *Sexual Pleasure*

The human being is a very complex organism. We have a physical body, an emotional response, an intellect and a spiritual aspect. We cannot ignore any one of these four elements. If we try to we are less than complete, less than perfect, less than whole. We need to look after our body, exercise it, feed it well and properly. We need to recognize our emotions, enjoy them, experience them, enrich and enhance them. Our intellect needs to be stimulated, challenged, expanded, increased and worked. Our spirituality needs to be expressed, nurtured and incorporated into our daily lives.

If we try to cut out any one of these aspects we can make ourselves seriously ill or depressed. Human happiness involves a constant search for an expression of these elements, a way of bringing them into harmony with each other, of utilizing them and improving them. Often that happiness fails if we ignore any of these aspects. The intellectual will denigrate emotional responses. The emotional type will neglect their mental powers. The athlete will fail to recognize the enormous power of their mind. The spiritual person will try to deny their physical body. Each will have a less than satisfactory relationship with their own inner harmony. Only by combining, by uniting, by implementing a holistic approach can we truly rise higher and attain perfection. Tantric sex is a unique way of achieving this perfection.

Tantric sex attempts to:

- **stimulate** the intellect by study, research and education
- **rouse** the emotions by increasing satisfaction and pleasure
- **enable** the body to be used to its very limits of performance
- **encourage** and promote spiritual development and growth.

These are the four key words of any practice of tantric sex – stimulating, rousing, enabling and encouraging. Through the practice of sex the aim is to become fully and totally in harmony and thus to achieve perfection while still alive. It is not a hard path or an impossible one. It is easy if certain guidelines – as laid out in this book – are followed and the person attempting to achieve this holistic perfection approaches it with the right focus and state of mind. Tantric sex is not a way of getting easy sex or attracting a lover, although those may be unintentional benefits. Tantric sex is not a way of exercising any form of power over your partner. Neither is it a way of conducting any spiritual one-upmanship over your friends. Tantric sex is carried out quietly, privately, discreetly, enthusiastically, diligently and enjoyably.

The origins of tantric sex

This book is mainly concerned with tantric sex as it's practised in the West today. But as it was originally practised in the East it was very different. In Chapter 10 I'll be explaining all about traditional Tantra, which still has a small number of followers even now. Just keep in mind that when I talk about 'tantric sex' I'm referring to the modern Western style.

Who this book is for

So who is this book for? Surely tantric sex is for New Agers, ex-hippies or sexual deviants? Not at all. Tantric sex is for anyone who wants to:

* improve their sexual technique
* have more control over their sex life
* have more fun and pleasure
* unite their sexuality with their spirituality
* improve their emotional response during sex
* encourage and stimulate their intellectual approach to sexual matters
* understand more about human sexuality.

You're probably in there somewhere – we all are. Tantric sex is for anyone who genuinely wants to know how to make their sex better and to change the focus of sex from an unconscious pleasure-based one to a conscious spiritual-based one. But within that spiritually based focus there is also plenty of room for increasing pleasure. Tantric sex isn't all about being serious and solemn and forbidding. If you don't enjoy the practice you are unlikely to want to continue.

Couples

This book is designed for couples who are in stable and supportive relationships. Because you need two to really gain benefits from the practice of tantric sex it makes sense for couples to do it together. Although there are many exercises you can do alone the basic practice is for a couple. This book is aimed at heterosexual couples. There are books on same-sex tantric practice but this book is for heterosexual couples because that is what I am familiar with and I wouldn't presume to write about something outside my own experience. However, gay couples may certainly benefit from this book if they so desire.

Obviously, if a couple have only just got together they can use this book but it is primarily designed for couples who are in a long-term relationship because they invariably have already had a lot of sexual experience with each other and thus will be able to put into practice the exercises with a pre-knowledge of each other's sexual response. This is an important aspect of tantric sex – we have to know our partner pretty well if we are to move on to the next stages of sexual activity. If you have to spend a lot of time finding out how your partner responds then the practice of tantra will be too much of an effort.

There are couples who come together for a brief passing sexual experience and use tantric techniques. This may be tantric sex but I doubt that any lasting spiritual experience is being developed. For that to happen we do need to have a commitment to our partner to work together for a long-term spiritual goal. Casual sex using tantric techniques may be enjoyable, pleasurable, orgasmic and fun – but it isn't tantra.

Tantric sex is for grown-up couples who love each other passionately and devotedly; couples who are open, honest and trustworthy with each other. Tantric sex is a bit like the advice once given to me about using a computer for bookkeeping – if you have a system that isn't working a computer will mess it up faster. If your relationship is in any way having problems, tantric sex practices will mess it up faster. Tantric sex doesn't cure relationship problems. The relationship has to be strong in the first place or it will highlight the problem areas. You *both* have to be committed to furthering your sexuality and spirituality. You have to be completely sexually open with each other – if there are areas you are doubtful about you need to resolve them before you begin. Tantric sex can certainly improve your performance and enhance things like confidence, stamina, orgasm control and technique. What it can't do is patch up a shaky relationship; you can't make love by making love. Neither can it change someone's basic personality. If you are in a relationship with someone you don't trust and don't feel open with, tantric sex won't change that. Tantric sex only works really well when you both want to work with your sexuality to rise higher spiritually. If one of you is coerced, pressured or forced in any way into participating then it simply won't work. You can encourage, challenge, stimulate, motivate and persuade a sceptical or reluctant partner. What you can't do is blackmail them into taking part – and that means emotional blackmail as well.

When are we ready? There is a time for us to practice tantric sex – when we are ready. No amount of persuasion can make us ready when we plainly aren't. Trying to make someone take part when they aren't ready is damaging and unproduc-tive. You may have to wait. Someone may be sexually ready but spiritually not yet ready, or they may have the spiritual aspiration but not the sexual readiness. We can't force anyone to be ready before their time.

However, if you are both keen and prepared to 'have a go' then you should 'go for it'. Tantric sex will enhance your intellect, body, emotions and spirit. If you both approach it in the right frame of mind it will more than compensate for any inexperience or lack of knowledge.

Sexuality

What is sexuality? We all have intercourse. We all have orgasms. But what is sexuality? What are we setting out to improve? I think the key word for sexuality within the realms of tantra is *control*. We are setting out to control our sexuality. That doesn't mean limit but to have power over. To be able to operate within a sexual relationship with power and authority rather than being at the mercy of our desires and urges. The control of our sexuality is an important step in being able to control our spirituality. By exercising control over our bodies and our emotions we are better able to control our spirituality.

There is nothing in tantric sex that should offend us or make us shudder. Tantric sex is all quite normal and enjoyable. It is not designed for athletes, contortionists or perfect people. Tantric sex is for ordinary people, 'warts 'n' all'. There is nothing wicked, sinful, shameful or unnatural in tantric sex practices. You won't be called on to try anything deviant or peculiar. You won't be asked to perform beyond the capabilities of any normally healthy person (see page 9). Tantric sex practices require no more agility or strength than 'normal' sex. They may require a degree of calm, tranquillity and effortless movement that may seem unnatural at first, as we are used to reacting in the heat of passion and lust. Tantric sex, remember, is about control. When we are in control we can achieve much more than when we are at the mercy of our excitement.

Spirituality

So what are we talking about when we talk about spirituality with tantric sex? Is this a religion, a cult, a faith, a belief, a creed? No, not at all. By spirituality we mean a personal experience of that energy, that force which keeps us alive – the internal godhead if you like. There is no set of beliefs with tantric sex. There is only experience. You don't have to believe anything. You don't have to take on board anyone else's opinions or ideas or principles. If tantric sex works for you it will work in a very real and positive way. You don't have to believe anything. If you don't experience it, feel it, know it, then it isn't real.

Tantric sex is about experiencing the energy – sexual energy if you like – that we can feel moving within us, recharging, enervating, powering and vitalizing us. This energy – known as *kundalini* by the Hindus – is what we are setting out to experience, to know, to bring forth and enjoy. What we are seeking to do is unite the sexual energy with the spiritual energy, simultaneously. There may be other ways of doing this but the practice of tantra is gentle, easy, enjoyable, pleasurable, fun and practical. It works. People who practice tantra invariably find that their sexual performance improves and their spirituality is enhanced. They go a long way towards achieving that perfection, that total holistic union of mind, body, spirit and emotions. It makes them well-rounded people who are better able to deal with life, and enables them to have a deeper and more meaningful relationship with the people around them, especially their partner.

What this book sets out to achieve

So what are we setting out to achieve? Taking a couple who are open and honest with each other, who enjoy a deep and meaningful relationship and are committed to each other, what do we expect to see after they have completed a course of tantric sex? The answer is probably nothing. What they will have experienced depends entirely on what they have put in. And what the end result will be is completely indeterminate. Tantric sex practice is an ongoing process – there is no end product. There is no exam at the end of it. There is no test to take or qualification to gain. Only the couple can judge what they have achieved. Only the couple can determine what they have gained by their practice. And, in a sense, only the individuals in that relationship can judge what they have achieved for themselves.

So how do we judge success? That is a personal assessment. If, after a while of practising tantric sex techniques, you and your partner are enjoying sex more, have experienced some form of spiritual experience during sex and are feeling more comfortable with each other about sex, then you can quite legitimately state that you have had a measure of success. The problem comes when each partner has a completely different experience – one has gained while the other seems not to – or when 'nothing happens', i.e. during their tantric experience there is no heightened spiritual experience and the sex hasn't improved. Sometimes a couple (or perhaps only one of the partnership) has false expectations – they expect too much and are disappointed – or they set too high a goal that they fail to achieve or even simply expect what is not possible.

It is best to keep an open mind and to begin this journey with no expectations, apart from those you would have when anticipating a pleasurable trip. Only by experiencing what happens with a totally open mind, and heart, can real progress be made. Once you have expectations you are setting yourself up to fail or be disappointed. Tantric sex can be a mind-blowing experience or can be so subtle you miss it. Each and every tantric experience will be different; each will be unique and unrepeatable.

New realms of sexual experience

Mind-blowing? Subtle? What are we to expect if we are to have no expectations? Well, although we shouldn't have expectations of the spiritual experience, we can have expectations of the sexual experience. During tantric sexual practices we might find that we have achieved:

- simultaneous orgasms
- much more explosive orgasms
- whole-body orgasms
- multiple orgasms for men
- longer and more pleasurable sexual sessions
- more control over when and how we orgasm
- a shared emotional response to sex that goes deeper than anything we have experienced before
- heightened sexual excitement
- an increase in libido
- a more open and honest sexual relationship
- a deeper love and respect for our partner
- an ability to maintain sex sessions for longer and for them to be more enjoyable.

Not bad for a beginning – and then there is the spiritual side as well. Although we shouldn't have expectations of what we individually will experience we might find that we:

- feel our spiritual energy alive and vigorously moving within our body
- feel at one with the universe
- experience a deeper joy in being alive
- have an understanding of our 'soul' or 'spirit'
- establish a union with the 'One'
- experience a deep joy within us that lasts beyond the sexual activity
- feel a spiritual bond with our partner
- feel their spiritual energy moving
- share our spiritual energy with our partner
- understand more about our role or mission in life
- step outside of our normal experience and be made aware of a greater or bigger plan or picture
- fuse our spiritual body with our physical body to create a new, united, holistic being.

And yet each of these may be so subtle that we couldn't put our finger on any of it and say 'that happened' or 'this happened'. The whole spiritual experience may be one of merely feeling more enhanced and complete, a subtle and gentle acceptance of our spirituality. We may not find all the answers but we may find the questions no longer seem relevant.

Practical exercises

All the practical exercises in this book assume you have a 'normal' degree of physical and mental health. If you are in any doubt, please consult a qualified medical practitioner before you embark on any of them. Nothing will be asked of you that isn't possible, easy and practical but certain conditions do apply. For instance, anyone with a heart condition should see their medical practitioner and women in the later stages of pregnancy should be cautious of doing anything too athletic – again consult your practitioner if in any doubt. Anyone taking any medication should also consult a qualified medical practitioner.

There are cases where people have used recreational drugs during tantric sex practices. This is not something we could recommend. It is better to find the experience naturally and easily than to depend on a chemical experience that may ultimately be more harmful than beneficial. Natural is best.

Techniques

The techniques you'll find in this book have been developed in the USA, as well as the UK, mostly in the last 35 years. But, as already pointed out, they're derived from the Tantric tradition of India, as well as incorporating ideas from Chinese Taoism and Arab eroticism.

None of these techniques are difficult to acquire, nor do they require any particular skills other than an open mind, a willingness to try anything and a genuine desire to experience something new. They include specific techniques for men and women to try individually and for couples to try together. These techniques are designed for two reasons:

- to enhance one's own sexual performance
- to enhance the performance of the couple jointly.

For instance, you will find techniques to help men overcome premature ejaculation and to delay their orgasm. For women, there are techniques for improving their vaginal 'squeeze' and, for the couple, techniques to be carried out together while having sex. All these techniques are designed for a specific purpose and should be practised until you feel you have adequately understood and perfected them. But they should always be done for enjoyment and fun as well as for practical reasons. If you don't enjoy the journey you might not arrive at your destination.

Enjoyment is a key part of tantra. Sex is enjoyable, fun and exciting. There is nothing in tantra to suggest otherwise. By enjoyment we learn more, remember more and are more willing to try things again. If it all becomes too serious and academic we lose the element of fun and thus lose our way. By making things as enjoyable as possible we can have fun as well as learning. Fun often involves laughter. Laughter is a good part of both sex and tantra. We need to be able to see the funny side of things. We need to be able to laugh at ourselves and we need to be able to laugh when things go wrong. In tantra there is no failure – only finding a way that doesn't work. Once we have found *all* the ways that don't work we will have found success.

Summary

The holistic approach to human existence:

- mind
- body
- emotion
- spirit.

The fundamental aims of tantric sex:

- to stimulate the intellect
- to rouse the emotions
- to enable the body to achieve sexual satisfaction and heightened performance
- to encourage spiritual awareness.

Who this book is for – loving couples in long-term committed and stable relationships, couples who have achieved a good measure of openness and honesty with each other.

What tantric sex won't do:

- patch up a shaky relationship
- facilitate casual sex
- attract a lover
- change people's basic fundamental nature.

Being spiritually and sexually ready to try tantric sex practices.

What is sexuality and how will the practice of tantra assist it? – learning control.

What is spirituality and how will the practice of tantra assist it? – raising *kundalini* energy, experience the spirit within.

What this book sets out to achieve – judging success, false expectations, enjoying the journey.

New realms of sexual experience – learning new techniques to achieve:

- simultaneous orgasms
- more forceful and powerful orgasms
- multiple orgasms
- more sexual control
- deeper emotional response
- an experience of one's spirituality within oneself.

Practical exercises – nothing untoward or difficult, contacting a qualified medical practitioner if you are in any doubt about your health, a warning about recreational drugs.

Techniques – drawn from modern Western teaching which, in turn, is based on three main traditions:

- Hindu
- Taoist
- Arab.

Enjoying tantra – laughter, fun, not seeing things in terms of failure or success.

02

what is tantric sex?

In this chapter you will learn:
- the different forms of tantrism
- about tantric sex and sex manuals
- about ancient tantric texts.

The basic Hindu Tantric rites, for the ordinary worshipper, required the presence of several couples and their guru, who was there to see that ritual sex did not deteriorate into mere self-indulgence and that proper procedure was observed. Even so, the less than devout believer may well have viewed the ceremonial as a pleasant evening's entertainment, the equivalent of a stiff aperitif, a good dinner, and then bed.

Reay Tannahill, *Sex in History*

So what exactly is tantric sex?

The word *tantric* comes from the Sanskrit *tantra* which means 'a written text'. These texts were known as *threads* or *fundamentals* because their subject matter invariably concerned important issues such as sex, religion or the attainment of enlightenment. A tantra was the written equivalent to a *mantra* which was a spoken chant or prayer that could bring about a union with God if used correctly and repeatedly. Likewise, a *yantra* was a drawing or painting, usually geometric, that could achieve a similar result if studied hard enough or meditated upon.

Sex manuals

Very few tantric texts have been translated into English. In any case, for the general reader, they're rather boring. Far more accessible are those ancient manuals that come under the heading of 'sacred sex'. They are the Indian *Kama Sutra* and the *Ananga Ranga*, the Arabic *Perfumed Garden*, the Chinese 'pillow books' such as the *T'ung Hsuan Tzu (Tao of Sex)* and the Japanese *shunga* (spring drawings). You may well have heard of some if not all of these quite famous books, but how many people have actually read them? To be honest, they're quite difficult to read for Westerners. They were written a long time ago and have lost a lot both through translation and through the differences in culture. We must be careful not to dismiss them as antiquated and irrelevant texts that couldn't possibly have any bearing on our modern lives or be of any use to us. They do contain, often hidden in flowery or esoteric language, a vast wealth of practical, unusual and fascinating information about how we can improve our sex lives, alter the focus of our lovemaking and find a new satisfaction within a committed and lasting relationship.

Different forms of tantrism

Tantric sex has followed many different paths; there have been tantric Buddhists, tantric Hindus, tantric Taoists and even tantric agnostics. They invariably, albeit to differing degrees, use sex as a focus for channelling energy towards a higher or more spiritual end. In this book you will find a unique distillation of all the best techniques and practical exercises from the tantric texts of the past. There is no pressure to follow any particular path, neither is there any attempt to encourage you to do anything you may find difficult or for which you have any hesitation. Any of the practical assignments given in the following chapters are for your information – try as many or as few as you like. Those you enjoy or help you achieve a specific result you can keep; those you don't like or find unsatisfactory you can abandon.

Sex is an intensely personal experience and what suits one couple may be unhelpful to another. Feel free also to experiment, to take exercises further, to invent your own, to adapt, modify, change or improve any of the techniques you like. The tantric texts were not fixed rules but relied on growth and change to make them better. Likewise you can only learn by trial and error.

Hindu aims

The original tantric way was probably Hindu. The Hindus believed that there was a four-way path towards enlightenment. The first was *dharma* – following correct social and moral behaviour; this obviously varied depending on what caste you were or what profession you followed. The second of the aims was *artha* – material wealth and comfort. The third was *kama* – love and physical pleasure. The fourth was enlightenment itself – *moksha* – brought about by following the first three. We are interested here in the third of the four aims, which is *kama*. All the aims had various texts written about them which are known as the *sutras* or philosophies. Hence the *Kama Sutra* – the philosophy of love and physical pleasure – which we will look at more closely in a moment.

The religious focus of sex

The fact that the Hindus saw both material wealth and pleasure as being pathways to enlightenment often surprises or even shocks people from the West. The ancient Hindus saw comfort, food, drink and sex as being not only essential parts of the human psyche but also as unsuppressible urges. If they could not be suppressed then they ought to be put to good use; to be perfected and used as a focus for a higher or more spiritual life. They also saw human life as holistic – in other words there was no division between religion and everyday life. Every duty, every task, every indulgence could be carried out as a religious act of worship so that you didn't have to make a specific time or place for worship but could incorporate it into every facet of your life.

It makes sense to include God in your daily life, within every activity, rather than excluding the Divine until you're ready to pick it up again – after all, it is with us constantly anyway. The tantric practitioners were merely acknowledging something that we all know to be true – that there is no separation. Not only were they acknowledging it, they were using it to enjoy their lives and increase their opportunities to move forward on the fourfold path.

The *Kama Sutra*

About 2,000 years ago an Indian aristocrat and wise man called *Vatsyayana* collected the best of the Hindu erotic manuals around at that time and edited them into one volume that became known as the *Kama Sutra*. It was first published in English in 1883 by Forster Fitzgerald Arbuthnot and Sir Richard Burton, the famous explorer and, as you can imagine for its time, caused a considerable stir in the West. Nobody had ever seen anything quite like it and it generated an enormous amount of controversy – was it pornography or education? Various members of the Church declared it ungodly and demanded its immediate destruction. Luckily for us it survived.

The *Kama Sutra* book is not only a sex manual as we would think of it in modern terms but a guide to the right foods to eat before lovemaking, the right style of courtship, a recipe book of aphrodisiacs, an instruction guide for making love charms, a keep fit and exercise manual, a marriage guidance advice book and even a travel guide with advice on where to meet girls, avoid contagious diseases and the best places to buy sex aids.

Many people believe that the *Kama Sutra* is merely a collection of bizarre sexual positions, but it is much, much more. It includes discussions on health and marriage, how to attract a partner, how to avoid adultery, sensual and arousing kissing, embracing and very erotic foreplay. The book contains little in the way of moral judgements, allowing the reader to learn freely from it and select and practise the parts they want.

The *Kama Sutra* also contains a lot of information that is irrelevant today, such as how to charm your lover so you could sleep with them without their knowledge, how to dispose of your lover's marriage partner, the correct rituals for being introduced to prostitutes and some quite dangerous and poisonous love potions.

The *Khoka Shastra* and the *Ananga Ranga*

Although the *Kama Sutra* is probably the best known of the Hindu erotic texts it is actually only one of several, including the *Khoka Shastra* and the *Ananga Ranga*.

The *Khoka Shastra* was written by an Indian scholar called *Khokkoka*, possibly in the 12th century CE. It concentrates more on aspects of love rather than sexuality. It's more about sex within marriage and how to maintain and keep a long-term relationship sexually fresh and exciting.

The *Ananga Ranga* was written by *Kalyaanamalla*, possibly in the 16th century, and was soon translated into Arabic where it became one of the most important Arabic sexual texts. It deals in detail with the sexual positions and updates the techniques of the earlier works.

By looking at the material available in all three volumes you can gain a considerable insight into Indian culture – such as more experimental lovemaking, enjoying sex in a long-term relationship, prolonging and enhancing foreplay, as well as an understanding of some of the Hindu sects such as the cult of *Shiva* and the symbolism of the phallic *lingam*.

Buddhist tantric practices

We can also explore an exciting and different version of tantric sex, practised by the secret and little-known Tibetan Buddhist sect which is dedicated to a union with God, through orgasm, by raising *kundalini* energy. Tantric Buddhism is the much misunderstood practice of using the sexual energy as a way of exploring spirituality. It includes techniques for prolonging intercourse, which can be easily learnt and practised. Some of the, until now, most secret techniques are revealed and explained so that we can incorporate them into our lovemaking and uniquely combine sex with spirituality – using sex as a gateway to a richer and deeper spiritual experience and using spirituality as a means of expanding the sex act into one of erotic symbolism and meditation.

The techniques revealed have been shrouded in mystery for centuries. Here they are presented in a clear and easily understood way and include descriptions of the *chakras*, or energy centres, that are situated throughout the human body and the part they play in the *kundalini* energy's rise from the genitals to the higher spiritual centres in the brain.

The tantric Buddhists believe that we contain vast stores of dormant energy that lie sleeping in the area of our genitals, coiled like a serpent – the *kundalini* – and that, through sex, the energy can be woken, guided and used to increase our vitality, health and spiritual experience and, ultimately, that tantra, the Divine reunion, can be completed.

The tantric Buddhists picked up on the Hindu ideas and adapted and refined them beyond most humans' expectations. Few of us today would be prepared to devote quite so much time (the rest of our lives) to the pursuit of enlightenment through sex alone, yet there is much we can learn from the Tantric Buddhists.

Chinese tantric practices

Around 750 CE *Pu K'ung*, a Chinese traveller, is reputed to have taken tantrism to China where he is regarded as the father of tantric Taoism. He had learnt about tantra in Ceylon (now Sri Lanka). However, Taoism – the ancient religion of China – predates even the *Kama Sutra*, and the Chinese Taoists' knowledge of sexual matters was already highly developed before the concept of tantra ever entered China. The fundamental principles of Taoism are that there must be balance and harmony in all things and that the entire universe is composed of energy, both male and female, yang and yin, which flows and is exchanged continually. This applies to sexual union as much as any other part of life.

The early Taoists wrote much on sexual matters and explored how the energy moves between partners. The Taoist approach is that sex is one of the basic forces of nature and shouldn't be repressed or denied but instead should be used to promote health, longevity and happiness. The longer each sexual union goes on the more energy is generated. The Taoists explored in great detail how to prolong sex so that the maximum benefit could be gained.

The Taoists produced pillow books designed as instructional manuals to help lovers enjoy sex. The oldest of these are probably the sections of the *Huang-ti Nei Ching Su Wen* (the Yellow Emperor's classic of internal medicine) devoted to sex. It takes the form of a question and answer dialogue between *Huang Ti*, the Yellow Emperor, and one of his ministers, *Ch'i Po*, in which the Emperor asks questions and the minister gives answers on diet, lifestyle, moral codes, hygiene and ethics. His answers on sex are refreshingly open and liberated. He explains how the energy exchange that takes place between men and women during sex can be used to promote health and longevity. The philosophy of Taoism includes such interesting sexual positions as the *Kicking Donkey*, *Lady Yin and the White Tiger* and *Two Ducks Flying* and the sexual organs are unusually described as, for men, the *Jade Stem* or the *Heavenly Dragon* and, for women, the *Vermilion Gate* or the *Jade Pavilion*. So when the Heavenly Dragon enters the Jade Pavilion you can expect the *Great Bursting of the Clouds*.

Arabic tantric practices

The Arabian empire had its own version of sacred sex – the *Perfumed Garden* – not only a delightful book of advanced sexual techniques but also a treatise on moral, social and dietary advice. This book was written around 1600 CE when *Sheikh Umar ibn Muhammed alNefzawi* was commissioned by the *Grand Vizier of Tunisia* (then part of the Turkish Ottoman empire) to write a manual on the arts and techniques of love. Thus commanded, Nefzawi wrote the *Perfumed Garden* and it is still one of the best known erotic sex manuals in the world.

Nefzawi was a devout Muslim who saw sex as an example of God's sacred work and thus something to be enjoyed as a celebration of His gifts. Because of the Muslim disapproval of divorce, adultery being the third greatest sin of Islam after being an unbeliever or a murderer, the *Perfumed Garden* explores in some detail the role of sexuality in marriage and contains many useful and inventive techniques for stimulating and arousing your partner. This can help us keep the sexual excitement new and fresh during a long-term relationship. It also contains some wonderful descriptions of 11 classic positions, such as the

Rainbow Arch and the *Pounding on the Spot*, and six arousing movements such as the *Seducer*, the *Race of the Member* and *Love's Tailor* – with the advice to 'try each and all of them and settle for the ones which give both of you the greatest pleasure'.

Japanese tantric practices

Another area we will explore in some depth is the role eroticism plays in tantric sexuality. This is an area the Japanese have previously researched extensively and we can learn a great deal about our sexuality from their colourful and explicit *shunga*, or 'spring drawings'. These were given to young newlyweds on the first night of their honeymoon so that they could approach their first sexual experiences well prepared with visual aids. The drawings in the *shunga* may be considered explicit by Western standards, perhaps even pornographic, as they invariably have enlarged or heavily emphasized genitalia. However, this was only partly titillation – they were mainly to be used as an instruction manual.

Lovers could laugh together over the drawings and, if there was any embarrassment, they could point to positions they wanted to try without having to discuss anything. The tradition of the *shunga* only began to die out in the early part of this century, but in recent years they have begun to be revived as people realize that young couples don't know everything – far from it – when it comes to matters of sex.

The *shunga* also feature erotic aids and oral sex in a very free and uninhibited way. The *shunga* focus heavily on the art of the erotic as a means of stimulating sexual passion and this is derived from the ancient religion of Japan, Shinto, which says that sexual pleasure is the greatest of all – and therefore should be enjoyed as frequently as possible as well as in the most exciting way. The word *Shinto* is of Chinese origin – the Japanese way of describing Shinto is *Kami no Michi*, which means the Way of the Gods, for the followers of Shinto see everything in nature as imbued with the spirits of the Gods. It is a very ancient religion and there is evidence that it was alive and active during the Stone Age. It has come down to us through the centuries with an organized priesthood and colourful ceremonies and rituals that reflect its basic joyous nature – there is little sense of sin. It is essentially a religion of gratitude and love.

The energy of sex

Much of what you will learn in the following chapters concerns the movement of energy – *kundalini* to the Hindus, *ch'i* to the Taoists – and it is necessary to have a thorough grounding in the philosophies behind these concepts if you are to make real use of the techniques. We will explore the Taoist ideas of *yin* (female) and *yang* (male) energy and how we are all a unique blend of both, as well as the Hindu concept of the *chakras*, energy centres situated throughout the body. We will learn how to explore this energy, how to begin to use it to raise our consciousness, how to channel it and how to increase it, all through the enjoyable and exciting path of sexual awareness.

Stable and loving relationships

As previously stated, this book is written mainly for couples who are in a stable and loving relationship. Practising these techniques with someone who is not on the same wavelength is not only pointless but could hinder your progress rather than help it. Although you will find some exercises you can practise on your own, these are for learning about the energy and how your body functions rather than just being focused techniques.

Unrewarding experiences

One of the fundamental differences between the Eastern and Western approach to sex is the concept of a goal or end product. In the West, sex is seen as something that ends in orgasm and without orgasm is a disappointing or unrewarding experience. In the East, sex is seen as a pleasurable journey; there may be no need of orgasm because the pleasure has been too intense already.

One of the key aspects to tantric sex which cannot be overstated is the need for enjoyment. We all enter the bedroom with an agenda – perhaps it is as simple as having an orgasm. But it might be much more complex: getting our partner to act out a particular fantasy, wearing certain clothing or asking our partner to do something to us that we desire to have done or to be the sort of person we want them to be in bed, acting out some roleplay or performing in a certain way. Once we have this agenda our sexual activities can only be disappointing because our lover will never fulfil all our agenda – it just isn't possible unless they are a mindreader, contortionist, inexhaustible or perfect. They will never be all these things. How much better to start sex with no agenda beyond enjoying yourself.

Once we have this goal – enjoyment only – we allow our lover to express themselves fully and we can do anything we want as we go. Enjoyment as a goal means we allow the flow of sex to happen naturally and spontaneously. Good sex, tantric sex, relies very much on picking up on our partner's mood, their emotional state, their mental state, their physical state. If we already have an agenda then we are not regarding them with sufficient respect, not allowing them their own flow. By going with that sexual flow we can relax and enjoy so much more.

Male sexuality

The other fundamental difference concerns male sexuality. In the West, a male ejaculation is regarded as the same as his orgasm; in the East, a man's orgasm is something regarded as happening mostly without ejaculation. If the two happen simultaneously then that's a bonus or a deliberate act – one that is chosen rather than, as in the West, happens spontaneously and without control. The idea of the male orgasm without ejaculation is something so alien to Western thinking that many men do not believe it to be possible. In this book men can learn the techniques to achieve orgasm without ejaculation.

Divine energy

The tantric texts offer a wide and varied, sometimes conflicting, body of advice concerning human sexuality; but the one area they all agree on is the importance of sex within a loving and stable relationship. To the tantric practitioners, sex is not merely about a simple act of pleasure but a deep and profound exchange of energy. This energy – whatever you want to call it – is regarded as divine, a part of the energy of God or the fundamental principle of the cosmos – again whatever you want to call it – spirit, soul, *ch'i*, *kundalini*, yogic lifeforce. Thus when you are having sex with someone you are taking part in both a physical exchange of energy and a spiritual act of worship. By exchanging energy you are acknowledging what that energy is, its importance and its divinity. You aren't merely indulging in an act of procreation but an act of ultimate love. When you have sex with someone you are not only sharing their energy with yours but also sharing the energy of all your past lovers and all of theirs. This exchange or sharing of energy thus can be confusing and emotionally draining. If you have had a lot of lovers with whom sex has been unsatisfactory, abusive or degrading then that energy is being assimilated by your current lover. They will need to work hard to shake off the feelings you carry with you. And it's not only your own personal energy but also the fact that we are all products of our upbringing – we all carry a sexual inheritance from our culture, our parents, our society. That sexual inheritance can make us inhibited, repressed, self-conscious and sexually reserved.

Becoming sexually free

Before you can love another human being on such an intense and spiritual level you have to acknowledge that energy within yourself. Before loving another you have to be able to love yourself. As human beings we are bound up with guilt and embarrassment about our sexuality. This is part of our upbringing in the West. We are the inheritors of 2,000 years of sexual bigotry and repression and it isn't easy to shake that off quickly.

However, shake it off we must if we are to take our true places as sexual beings who are capable of giving and receiving love on such an intimate and personal level. Before we can offer someone else the perfect gift of our bodies we have to be able to love that body as much as we will expect our lover to appreciate it. This is often a problem. Because of the nature of Western society we are brought up with a whole range of concepts about physical perfection. What woman hasn't despaired that she no longer looks as trim as the fashion models in the magazines? What man doesn't lament his hair loss or regret his expanding waistline? But our lovers are, on a very deep level, not seeking us out for our physical personae but as vessels of that divine energy – and as such we are perfect. And if you are getting larger then you might just be containing more of that energy to share with your partner.

Being comfortable with your body

For real tantric sex to happen you have to be both comfortable and happy with your body. It's no good wanting to be a sexually divine lover when you want to keep the lights off, hide under the covers and keep your clothes on – and just because there are a few stretch marks or some added poundage. Remember, your lover loves you as you are. They don't care whether you match up to some mythical image of beauty or thinness. They care only that you love them and are with them. If they are trying to change your physical self then they might not be quite on the same wavelength as you.

Practical assignment: Personal objective

Although this exercise might at first glance appear silly or unimportant what it reveals is the inner you and how you feel about yourself. When you are on your own find a full-length mirror and stand naked in front of it. Look objectively at yourself and hear what goes on in your mind.

What you see is unimportant – it is only a container – but what you say to yourself is the revealing information. Are you OK about standing there in the nude? Do you feel free and liberated? Or guilty and shy? Only you can know what goes on in your head. But remember that this is what your lover sees when they make love with you – not the outer body but with their lover's heart they can see all the stuff you carry around inside your head about your sexuality. That's what we've got to get rid of – all that stuff. And it's no good blaming anyone else: 'Oh, my mother made me feel this way about sex'; 'If it hadn't been for my first bad sexual encounter I'd be much more relaxed'; 'I've been hurt so many times I just can't trust any more.' When you stand naked in front of that mirror none of those people will be there.

Changing ourselves

That's why it's no good blaming them – they're not there any more – it's just you, your sexuality and that energy. Only you can change it. Even if you managed to get all the people responsible for the way you feel about sex together and you could accuse them, blame them and harangue them, it wouldn't do you one iota of good – because only you can change what goes on inside your head. *Only you*. And the first change you can make is *acceptance*. What you see is what you get – for better or worse – it's what you get – what your lover gets – and they love you just as you are. Stand and look and be proud. What you see, believe it or not, is a perfect human being. You are exactly as your creator wanted you to be. How can you dare argue with your creator? If they don't know what they're doing what hope have the rest of us got? According to the tantric practitioners what you see is a perfect representation of that energy, that divinity in a human form. Isn't it fabulous?

The perfect you

And it's exactly as it was supposed to be – not too fat nor too thin, not too tall nor too short, not too old and not too young. Every line, every wrinkle, every blemish was put there to serve you, to improve you, to help you manifest in your glory. Be happy with what you see, be proud of the nakedness of the pure *you*. The world will not see your like again because there's only one of you, perfect and unique. Enjoy.

Tantric sex is about appreciation

Tantric sex is about using sex to increase, improve, expand, explore and enjoy one's spirituality. It's not about casual encounters, group orgies, roleplaying, role models or even ego enhancement. Purely and simply it's about *appreciation*. Appreciating that the lover you are with is a container of divine energy and, as such, a perfect complement to your own energy. We will look in more detail later at male and female energy but for the moment you have to remember that you are a container of male or female energy and you need the balance of the opposite type.

Celibacy has no place in a book on tantric sex. No sex is as bad as unsatisfactory sex – and both are about the disharmony of energy exchange. How many times have you had sex and felt worse afterwards? Recognizing the importance of the energy exchanged, generated and enhanced is the first lesson of tantric sex.

Practical assignment: Expectation

With your lover write down all your expectations of your partner. What do you want them to give you, do for you? What do they do that you don't like? What do you want to do that you've never dared ask or try? How do you want to be held? What sort of caresses do you like to give and receive?

Learning about your partner

When you have written down everything you can think of swap over. What you will be given will invariably, unless you're very connected, be a surprise. This exercise mustn't become the beginning of discord or argument. Instead you can learn a lot about your partner from it. Whatever your partner wants, expects, gives or receives is fine – and the same goes for you. In tantric sex there can be no right or wrong – only acceptance and recognition.

You have to do this practical assignment with two things in mind: honesty and no judgements. If you want to be in harmony with your partner you have to be honest – as they do also. And if they've been courageous enough to be honest then you have to accept what they say without judgement. A person's sexuality is a very vulnerable and delicate area – but there is no right or wrong. If they have certain reservations or what may appear to you to be strange notions or ideas, then what they feel is fine – because it's part of them. Obviously the same goes for you – your feelings, ideas and wants are to be respected.

Asking for what we want

Look at what you partner has written. Did you know all this? If not, what were you thinking of? The tantric texts were written as a means of communication. Enhancing sex is about just this – *communication*. This communication between lovers can be spoken or not – just so long as it takes place. We all need to be cared for, comforted, loved, caressed and worshipped – but how many of us know how to ask for these things? Or indeed that it is our right to expect them? But first we have to be prepared to give them. We cannot give unless we know what is wanted of us, what is expected. To know that we have to be prepared to listen, to be aware of our partner's needs. We cannot be open to another's needs if we are consumed with our own. To give wholeheartedly, without reservation, without expectation of reward or reciprocal gifts is the first and hardest lesson of tantric sex.

When we are aware that our partner's needs are ultimately important we can give ultimately to them. And thus they will give back to us unconditionally. We cannot expect this return of love – it's a bonus when it happens. But we have to be the ones to make the first declaration of unconditional worship – that's the way it works. We give first and then are rewarded – sometimes. But we always give first.

Taking and receiving

Western sex is about taking first, tantric sex is about giving first. We must give away some of ourselves before there's any space to receive something of somebody else. And we need that something if we are to be truly realized, well-rounded and complete human beings.

If your partner is not truly and totally sexually satisfied how can you expect them to be harmonious enough to please you? This works for both of you by the way. Neither one of you can say, 'you have to give to me first'. We must be both ready to give to each other at the same time. Giving can be one of the most rewarding of all activities – and not something we are used to in the West where the 'me first' attitude has deprived us all of a richer experience. Giving to our lover also means we must make time – for them.

Practical assignment: Worshipping our lover

You can try this one on alternate days or nights. The beauty of this practical assignment is that there is no going first. Whoever gives first, receives first also. Let's suppose it's the woman who is to receive first. Your partner should run you a warm bath and prepare the bathroom with incense and candles. Make an occasion of it. You can relax and enjoy the bath while your lover washes you all over. Tell them how you like your hair washed, let them do it for you. You are being worshipped as a representation of the ultimate female energy. You are receiving. But your partner is also receiving. In his act of worship he is receiving an opportunity to do service, to be allowed to be of use. He is receiving just as much as you but in a different way.

After your bath you should find somewhere warm to lie down – perhaps on a rug in front of the fire. Your lover can then massage you with essential oils. This is not a therapeutic massage to ease muscular aches and tension (although it may well do that as a bonus) but rather a massage so your lover can explore your body, caress you in a non-sexual way. He should touch and soothe every part of your body until you feel your skin shine and burst with energy. Tell him how you feel as you go, which bits feel best, where you like being touched most, how much pressure to use, how his hands feel on your body. This massage usually produces a warm soporific effect but can also induce a sexual tension as well.

Let your lover bring you to orgasm if you like by using his fingers, tongue and mouth. But this exercise is not about having sex, it's about caressing, exploring and touching. Let him do all the touching. If you want him naked as well that's fine, but it's a massage for you. You don't have to attend to his sexual needs in any way. This is his opportunity to worship the female divinity in you – the *Shakti* or Goddess. Enjoy the feeling of not only being worshipped but also being the Goddess herself in human form – for that's what you are and as such entitled to be worshipped.

The next day it's the man's turn to be worshipped. Let your partner bathe and wash you, and let them give you the same soothing massage. Tell them which bits you like touched, where you feel warmth and caresses from their hands. You are being worshipped as the representation in human form of the God *Shiva*, for that's what you are.

If you want to you can let your partner bring you to orgasm using her hands and mouth, but remember, and this is important for men, real sex is not about orgasm. Tantric sex is about the energy generated by and during sex – and that is something separate from the male orgasm. In the West, we are very goal oriented. We believe that every sexual encounter must end in orgasm or we will not be satisfied or fulfilled. However, this is simply not true. There are many practitioners of tantric sex who have refrained for years from ejaculating (which in the West we equate with orgasm) without losing anything from their sex lives; rather they have gained immeasurably.

Once we lose the need to be so focused on our orgasm we can begin to enjoy the journey. However, since we are just starting out you can still have your orgasm for this practical assignment, but it might be beneficial to try it again on another occasion and to decide not to have an orgasm deliberately and see how it feels. We will look at enhancing the male orgasm later. You may find the exercise feels more satisfying because it has no end, no conclusion. If it ends in orgasm there is then a need to find another focus, to move on to something else. But if it doesn't end in orgasm then the feeling of being worshipped as Shiva continues, the afterglow remains as a glow.

Loving relationships

So how necessary to tantric sex is a loving relationship? Well, the practitioners of tantra would say that if you don't have time to learn about your partner you cannot know them. If you don't know them, and their sexual preferences and needs, you can't be a good lover. The idea of a 'one-night stand' to the practitioners of modern tantra would be quite abhorrent (although not, as we'll see, to its ancient adherents). How can you learn everything you need to know in one night? And if you're not learning about your partner's needs what are you doing? Surely then you must be going for purely selfish sexual gratification? If that's the case, then the energy will be all wrong. You can't share energy if you're thinking only of your own needs. The need for a stable relationship becomes increasingly important in this day of sexually transmitted diseases and potentially fatal ones.

Energy trails

The whole idea of energy exchange during sexual activity is fairly new to the West; however, it has long been recognized in the East. The energy exchange is on a permanent basis. You carry with you all the energy trails of all your past lovers. If your sexual encounters are brief and hurried, or shameful and negative, then that's the sort of energy you will be carrying and passing on to your next lover. They in turn will inherit that energy. The cycle has to stop somewhere. In the next few chapters you can learn how to purify or alter that energy, turning it from cold and negative into warm and loving – something you'd be proud to share with another person.

Summary

Tantra means a written text. Not many tantric texts have been translated into English but you can consult the following books on 'sacred sex':

- the *Kama Sutra*
- the *Ananga Ranga*
- the *Perfumed Garden*
- the Chinese pillow books such as the *T'ung Hsuan Tzu*
- the Japanese *shunga* (spring drawings).

The different forms of tantric are Hindu, Taoist, Arabic, Tibetan Buddhist and modern Western traditions.

The Hindu aims of *dharma*, *artha*, *kama* and *kaivalya* which bring about enlightenment. The Hindu approach to sex is one of an unsuppressible urge which could be sublimated towards a spiritual end.

The Tibetan Buddhist practices of raising *kundalini* energy – the serpent energy – to prolong intercourse. The role the chakras play – the seven energy centres located throughout the body – in helping raise the *kundalini* energy.

The Taoist practices of how energy moves between the two partners in any sex act and how that energy – *yin* (female) and *yang* (male) can be used to enhance sex and progress spirituality.

Arabic sexual practices as an example of God's sacred work and something to be enjoyed as a celebration, a gift.

Japanese tantric practices which include Shinto practices of erotic sex and foreplay. The joyous nature of Shinto where nothing is regarded as 'sin'.

The energy of sex – how we exchange energy with our partner, the necessity of a loving and stable relationship, picking up on our partner's mood, the residue energy of previous sexual encounters we carry with us.

Male sexuality and the tantric approach of the non-ejaculatory orgasm for men.

Divine energy and how having sex can provide an exchange of divine energy and a spiritual act of worship.

Our sexual inheritance – what we have brought with us from our culture, our upbringing, our parents, our society and how this can repress us, inhibit us or make us sexually reserved. The need for sexual freedom. How to learn to love ourselves before we can love others.

Being comfortable with our body. Practical assignment – standing naked in front of a mirror to learnt to accept ourselves as our lover sees us. Appreciating the divine energy within us and loving ourselves as a receptacle of that energy.

Practical assignment – writing down all your sexual preferences, likes and dislikes, needs and wants and sharing this with your lover. Your lover does this and shares it with you. This is tantric sexual communication and can help clear up any areas of misunderstanding and confusion. You'll both know what each other needs and likes rather than floundering in the dark. This is asking for what you want.

Practical assignment – giving and receiving. Each taking turns to be worshipped, to be adored, to be bathed and caressed.

03

benefits of tantric sex

In this chapter you will learn:
- how to enhance your spirituality
- how to be a better, more considerate lover
- about the pleasure principle.

Tantra does not want you to sleepwalk through your life. Staying awake means taking risks, being different, being yourself.

Ecstasy is actually a revolutionary act. People who know how to fully enjoy themselves are true voluntary consumers. They need only to be themselves to be happy. The pursuit of happiness which, by definition, never ends, does not fascinate them.

David and Ellen Ramsdale, *Sexual Energy Ecstasy*

Obviously, if we are about to embark on an intensive course of tantric sex we need to know in advance why we should be doing this. There is nothing worse than investing a lot of time and effort if we don't know why and are thus unable to ascertain whether we have indeed been successful.

There are various reasons why we would like to improve our sexual techniques and combine our sexual activities with a furthering of our spiritual existence. For instance, there are those of us who seek a greater and more harmonious balance between pleasure and spirit – sex and spirituality give us a perfect union between body and soul. For some there is a genuine desire to enhance their sexual performance and using tantric practices certainly will do this. For others there is a need to find out more about their spiritual life and again tantric practices will help in this.

What we mustn't do is start on a course like this without being sure of our motives. It simply isn't good enough to have a vague notion of 'it seems like a good idea'. We have to be committed and certain that this is what we want to do, otherwise we will lose interest and lack motivation. Likewise being pressurized will do us no good. We have to have our own motivation and not just be going along with something because our partner wants to. Both partners need to be motivated, committed and enthusiastic. The best results come about when this happens.

Tantric sex is a way of exploring not only your own sexuality and spirituality but also that of your partner. Together you can achieve much but you must both be fully committed or the enthusiasm will wane. That isn't because tantric sex is necessarily difficult or extreme, but merely because it requires a particular focus, a need to pay attention to the exercises and a commitment of time and energy.

Improvements in relationships

Once tantric sex becomes second nature there will be an improvement in your relationship. Tantric sex encourages honesty and openness. It requires couples to communicate with one another on a level that previously wouldn't have happened or even be thought possible. Once, together, you have experienced bliss and ecstasy it cements the relationship in a way that nothing else can. Nothing else has quite the same impact as tantric orgasms experienced in a state of total oneness and togetherness. Practising tantric sex requires you to be open, honest, thoughtful, sensitive, considerate and respectful. You both have to consider how each other feels about sex and spirituality. You are embarking on a considerable journey of self-discovery and exploration. To do this together means you have to be not only lovers but also friends. Regarding your partner as your best friend is a good starting point, but it may be something that emerges naturally from this journey.

Better sex

When we first start out on our sexual life we fumble around a lot, have some pretty uncertain and unsatisfactory encounters, make mistakes, get it wrong, do it badly and generally have a sort of 'make it up as we go along' philosophy. This works for a while until, as we get older and wiser, we realize that we aren't doing as well as we might. We settle into our first long-term relationship and learn a lot from our partner. We might even invest in a few modern Western sex manuals to help things along. But it is very rare for us actually to go out of our way to learn more. We are, to a certain extent, still fumbling in the dark.

Tantric sex throws a light on sex. It sets out to teach us how to be real sexperts. If we are going to have a long and varied sex life then it makes sense to learn and understand ourselves intimately as sexual beings. There is nothing wrong with sex. There is nothing wrong with fumbling along. But we can go further. We can become good lovers, even excellent ones.

If we have a computer, we constantly upgrade it because we want the best, the fastest, the slickest. It should be the same with sex. We should want to do it to the very best of our ability. OK, so sometimes we might like to take time out and just have plain old sex with no spiritual focus – there is nothing wrong with a sexual romp purely for pleasure, a quick snatched sexual encounter with our partner with none of the ritual or preparation that tantric sex requires. That's all fine. A hasty burger grabbed in a fast food outlet is sometimes exactly what we need rather than a full five course meal served with wine and by candlelight. But learning tantric sex does give us the option to become gourmets, connoisseurs of the finest, specialists in our chosen interest – sex. The techniques involved aren't complicated or bizarre. They have been used over many centuries by thousands of ordinary people to enhance their sex lives with considerable success.

If we are going to do sex then let's do it well. Let's do it properly. Let's make it the most wonderful, satisfactory, fabulous experience we can. Let's invest some time and effort in learning how it really can be, rather than settling for second best – the fumbling in the dark. Most people accept that, on a scale of one to ten, their sex life is around six or seven at best. Once you learn tantric techniques you realize that the scale actually goes up to 100 which makes settling for a six or seven pretty poor really. Let's, instead, aim for the high nineties and really achieve sexual ecstasy!

Enhanced spirituality

The aim of tantric sex is to enhance one's spirituality. Using the pleasure principle to further our awareness of our inner spirituality makes perfect sense. There is no suppression in tantric sex, no sublimation, no false squashing of our natural desires and needs. Tantric sex allows us the freedom to be ourselves, to enjoy, to be happy and at the same time to achieve or obtain some form of spiritual integration.

Tantra doesn't require of us any belief system or religious belonging. Whatever your views of God, the universe or spirituality, they don't matter in this context. What tantra sets out to do is give the participant a direct experience of their own inner spirituality. Whatever happens is as a result of what is being done, what is being experienced. This way there can be no mistake about what is or isn't experienced. You don't have to believe anything nor do you have to have faith. As a result of practising the tantric techniques you have an experience. Whatever that experience is, it is yours and yours alone. It cannot be refuted or denied by anyone else. Within us is a subtle energy, an energy which has been clearly outlined in the ancient Taoist and Hindu texts. Tantric sexual practices allow us to have a direct experience of that energy. This experience is real. It happens – or doesn't happen, depending entirely on the individual – within oneself. It is a direct experience. You will feel and sense this energy. Whatever labels or titles or names you choose to put upon this energy is entirely up to you. For me it is sufficient to talk in terms of energy. Others prefer to speak of spirit, soul or internal divinity. Whatever we call it, whatever our views of it, it follows its own path, flows along its own meridians and can only be experienced.

Tranquillity

Once that energy has been experienced it puts a lot of what has happened in our life into perspective. Many tantric practitioners report that their lives enter a new stage of tranquillity after they have experienced this energy. It is not like all your questions get answered so much as all your questions seem irrelevant. You have been touched and have touched something so fundamental and so basic and raw that life can never be quite the same again. The energy, once experienced, once tasted, remains constantly in focus. One glimpse of heaven is sufficient to remind us that heaven exists forever.

Freedom from being orgasm driven

In tantric sex we aren't after bigger or better orgasms – although that may well be a side-effect or a bonus. What we want is the sensation of that energy felt within the orgasm or behind it or around it. Someone once said that an orgasm is like shining a flash of light across the face of God. In tantric sex what we are aiming at is keeping that flash on so that it becomes a searchlight. Having the orgasm may be pleasurable, enjoyable, a blissful relief, but not having it can be likewise. The bliss of the orgasm isn't in the physical aspect but in the spiritual one that accompanies it. For the vast majority of people the orgasm is only physical. Tantric practitioners seek the accompanying spiritual orgasm. If we can heighten the orgasm, extend it, lengthen it and enhance it, then the accompanying experience of that inner energy also gets heightened. And that experience is the aim. Thus the orgasm becomes a means to an end and not the end in itself. When we speak of multiorgasms we aren't interested in the physical aspect – although that is extremely pleasurable and ecstatic – so much as having the experience of the spiritual.

The pleasure principle

The experience is not spiritual in a religious sense. It encourages a sense of wellbeing, a glow of personal inner contentment. We may well achieve the same experience through intensive meditation, dance, ritual, withdrawal from the world, fasting, prayer and other spiritual systems. All of these are valid and produce results. All of these have been used at different times to differing effects, but all work, all are valid. The only difference is a matter of choice. At each stage of our lives a different approach may be used. At this stage the pleasure principle may well be the one that turns us on. Why sit alone in a room meditating when you can share the experience with your partner while having glorious and pleasurable sex? Experiencing that energy is the important thing, not the route to it. Sometimes we get hung up on the map and forget the ultimate destination. With tantric sex the map is passion and the destination is an experience of that inner energy while having an outer experience of pleasure and sex and enjoyment.

Being a better lover

If the map is passion we had better learn to be more passionate. Being more passionate is about being better lovers – quicker to arouse and be aroused, more exciting and excited, more stimulated and stimulating, more caressed and more caressing, feeling and being felt, stroking and being stroked, kissing and being kissed. We have to learn how to give, to caress, to titillate, to excite, to flirt, to woo, to stimulate, to turn on, to arouse. Being a better lover is knowing our stuff – all the techniques imaginable, being creative, imaginative, inventive, thoughtful and focused. If we want to bring our partner to the greatest heights of passion and ecstasy then we had better know what we are doing. In later chapters we will look at how to improve our techniques and our performance. This isn't about being good at sex for its own sake – although that is the payoff – but about being good at sex so we can last longer and bring our lover to greater plateaux of passion and pleasure, so that they can experience that energy within themselves more deeply, more strongly and for longer. And they will be able to do the same for us. Together a couple can take each other further and higher.

Being more considerate

One aspect of becoming a better lover is your growing consideration for your partner – and theirs for you. You learn to be honest and open and engender a spirit of trust. This trust is necessary to tantric sex. It allows each of you to relax with the other, really to open your heart, mind and soul to another human being in a way that isn't usually possible even within a very close relationship. Together you can experience more than being a mere human being. Together you can experience something of the inner spirituality we all carry within us. Once you have done this with another human being it allows you to really care about them – you see yourselves linked. And that caring extends to other people, people with whom you have not been intimate on such a deep level. Once you have experienced that energy within you know it is there inside every human being and as such you feel warm and caring towards them all.

There are many such benefits from tantra that you will experience as you practise over the next few weeks.

The following chapters contain many practical assignments – some for you to do alone, others for you both to do together – which we hope you will enjoy and practise. Remember, the secret of tantra is enjoyment. If anything becomes a chore or feels wrong then stop doing it for a while and go and do something more pleasurable.

Summary

The benefits of tantric sex:

- being sure of our motives, being committed; enthusiasm, motivation
- openness, honesty, thoughtfulness, sensitivity, consideration, respect
- better sex – investing time and effort in becoming better lovers, learning better techniques, practising tantric practices
- enhanced spirituality – a direct experience of one's inner spirituality, the subtle energy, Taoist and Hindu texts
- tranquillity – putting our lives into perspective, the focus of the energy
- freedom from being orgasm driven – the bliss of the physical orgasms, a means to an end, the experience of the mystical

- the pleasure principle – other means of achieving the same result, sharing the experience with your partner, passion
- being a better lover – bringing our partner to new heights of pleasure, making the experience last longer
- being more considerate – growing consideration for our partner, opening our heart, mind and soul, caring for others, warmth and care.

04

the practice of tantric sex

There are three 'rules' to follow when doing sensate focus. The first is: Focus on your sensations. *The second is:* Keep your focus in the here and now, releasing all extraneous thoughts. *The third is:* Enjoy yourself without having any expectations of yourself or your partner.

You will find these three rules incredibly freeing – and they are also essential ingredients for good sex.

Michael Riskin and Anita Banker-Riskin,
Simultaneous Orgasm

What you have to do

In Chapters 05 to 08 we will work through what you actually have to do to learn tantric sex.

Chapter 05 begins with practical assignments for men. These should be carried out alone although you might like to practise with your partner initially to make sure you are doing them right or to gain encouragement. Many of them are exercises to be carried out on a regular basis.

Chapter 06 is also one of practical assignments, this time for women. Again, these should be carried out over a period of time and on a regular basis. Thus they are probably best done alone.

Chapter 07 is meditation for both of you. You can do these together or on your own.

Chapter 08 is practical assignments to be carried out together. These practical exercises should be done in a spirit of exploration and intrigue. Don't have expectations but sit back and see what happens.

Exercises and practical aspects

We have laid out the exercises in an easy-to-follow format. There is nothing difficult or complicated, although some of them may be new to you. Keep an open mind and approach them with enthusiasm and you may be surprised how beneficial they are even if they do seem new and unusual.

Arousal

A key part of tantric sex is arousal. If you aren't excited and aroused you will find having sex at any time more difficult. The anticipation of having sex in a new and unusual way – the tantric way – can often be a sufficient turn-on for most people. But arousal should be kept to a high pitch. It is important not to approach tantric sex in a cold, clinical or experimental manner. Even if you are on a journey of exploration it is still necessary to be excited and aroused.

Some people seem to think that tantric sex is lacking in excitement. They believe, quite wrongly, that tantric sex is a practice which somehow needs to eliminate the excitement aspect of sex to make it work. This couldn't be further from the truth. Tantric sex requires the same levels of arousal as any other sort of sex – perhaps more.

Foreplay

As with any other sort of sex, foreplay is essential to tantric sex. Foreplay is all part of arousal and we need to be aroused, excited and stimulated. A good routine of foreplay is essential – you have to make an effort to turn your partner on as they do for you. Good tantric sex should be extremely erotic – and thus foreplay plays an important part.

Orgasm

Many tantric practitioners and teachers stress the importance of non-ejaculatory orgasms for men while at the same time emphasizing the need for the woman to have multiorgasms. In Chapter 05 we offer several techniques for men to help them learn the non-ejaculatory orgasm. These are difficult techniques to learn and many men will never master them. This shouldn't be seen as a failure, but as a future goal which may or may not be attained. If it isn't, then that's fine.

Mutual pleasuring

A very important aspect of tantric sex is mutual pleasuring – mutual masturbation. The reason for this is to bring your partner to the brink of orgasm so they can experience the movement of the *kundalini* – the inner energy. If you are busy concentrating on your own sexual experience or orgasm it makes it that much harder to concentrate entirely on your partner's pleasure and rhythms.

For mutual masturbation to work you have to know each other pretty well – again a good reason for the practice of tantric sex to be recommended to couples in long-term loving and stable relationships – because the practice requires a degree of grown-upness about sex. You can't have too many hang-ups or inhibitions if you are to give your partner a lot of pleasure over and over again. You have to know what you are doing to bring them to the peak of orgasm and this means being very much in charge of your personal techniques. A lot of these will be put forward for you to learn in Chapter 08, but it is also something you need to understand fully yourself. If, for instance, the man reaches orgasm fairly quickly he will need to learn how to slow it down himself before he can expect his partner to be able to do so.

A big part of mutual pleasuring for tantric sex is communication. You need to be able to tell each other that you are nearing orgasm – and exactly how close this is – without sounding ridiculous or inadvertently funny. We will make suggestions for this in Chapter 08. In order to communicate this information you need to know your own cycles of orgasm very well. Following the practical assignments will help in this.

Lovemaking positions

Some people seem to think that the sexual positions in such texts as the *Perfumed Garden* or the *Kama Sutra* are for double-jointed people, contortionists or sexual athletes. Not true. The sexual positions are all easy to do once you have tried them. It is in the telling that they seem improbable or impossible. Once you've tried them yourself you will realize how simple they are – and not that different from others you will have already tried yourself anyway.

Bliss and spirituality

Obviously, one of the main benefits of practising tantric sex is an increased awareness of one's own spirituality. And along with this comes bliss. Bliss is a hard one to define. It is a state of complete knowing, as if the last parts of the jigsaw have been slotted into place and you feel a complete human being. We need to know who we are spiritually, and tantric sex completes this picture for us in a very real and practical way. We don't have to listen to anyone else's opinion or theories. We don't have to believe in anything or anyone. We don't have to have 'faith'. What we experience is real. It is our own experience and thus cannot be judged or even commented on by anyone else. This is bliss. This is total spiritual freedom.

Summary

Keeping an open mind and approaching the practical assignments with enthusiasm.

Arousal – the importance of excitement and arousal in tantric sex, not approaching tantric sex in a cold or analytical manner.

Foreplay – the importance of arousal, excitement and stimulation in good foreplay for tantric sex.

Orgasm – men shouldn't get hung up on the non-ejaculatory orgasm.

Mutual pleasuring – knowing your partner well, knowing your own physical responses, knowing how to give pleasure.

Lovemaking positions – not as hard as you thought, easy once tried.

Bliss and spirituality – finding a real experience of one's own spirituality without having to rely on anyone else's opinion or beliefs.

05

practical assignments for men

In this chapter you will learn:
- about the PC muscle and relevant exercises
- how to improve energy techniques
- how to store energy.

Just as when a man does a woman, a woman needs to touch a man with the purpose of having her hand feel pleasure. Stroking for an effect is usually much less pleasurable for your partner. Remember that if a man's cock is not hard, that does not mean he cannot feel pleasure. The nerve endings are still there, and if his penis is touched pleasurably, it can feel exquisite to him.

Steve and Vera Bodansky, *Extended Massive Orgasm*

It can be a daunting experience for men coming to tantric sex practices for the first time. It requires men to be totally open and honest about their sexual relationships and this can be a hard thing to do initially – but it gets easier. Tantric sex requires men to question pretty well every aspect of how they view women, women's sexuality and their own sexuality. It's an ongoing process that takes a lot of time and hard work but the rewards are more than worth it.

In this chapter we will look at the three aspects of male sexuality and tantra:

• performance techniques to increase ejaculation retention and strengthen orgasms
• energy techniques to enhance internal energy movements
• spirituality techniques to put you in touch with an inner experience.

In this chapter you will also find a lot of practical assignments to improve your own sexual techniques. These will, in time, make you a fantastic lover, but first we have to do some practical assignments on that other sexual organ you have – the mind.

Practical assignment: Self-loving 1

For this assignment all you need is yourself and a blindfold. Be alone in a warm room where you feel private and safe and aren't going to be interrupted. This practical assignment is best done in the morning when your *ch'i* energy is fresh and you are invigorated. Don't do this exercise on a full stomach, so only eat a light breakfast. Lie down in a comfortable position. You will need to be naked and feel easy with yourself. You are going to masturbate yourself to orgasm. We aren't interested in what happens in and to your body. Instead what we want to concentrate on is what goes on inside your head while you are pleasuring yourself.

Follow your thoughts. The idea behind the blindfold is both practical – to stop you seeing – and symbolic – to isolate you within the confines of your own mind. As you masturbate what images do you call to mind? What erotic pictures do you use/choose to excite you? Are these wholesome and honest or pornographic and debasing? There are no right or wrong answers – only the truth within you.

As you achieve orgasm, what goes through your mind? Where do you picture your semen going? How do you see your partner/lover in your mind as you climax?

This is a practical assignment to get you thinking about how you view sex and women, your sexuality and your partner. It isn't intended to be a judgement or a criticism. It is merely a way of discovering the truth within each of us.

This practical assignment is designed to get you thinking about your role as a man and as a lover. In the West, men grow up with a lot of conflicting information about women and how we are supposed to be with them. Our early years are influenced by many erotic images of women that seem to suggest that they are sexually open and available. When we start courting in our teens it quickly becomes evident that the opposite is true. Women, to teenage boys, are unavailable despite giving out all the right sexual turn ons. They dress provocatively but we aren't allowed to touch – well, maybe we touch a bit, fondling and that sort of thing, light petting. Our first sexual encounters are of the fumbling in the dark sort and yet we are supplied with an endless stream of pornographic images from films, adverts, books, magazine and such like. We are given two very strong and very opposite views of women – that they are *not* sexually available and that they *are* sexually available. Which is true? Both of course and the answer lies in respect. When we respect women their sexuality is acknowledged as their own – they are independent of us and thus separate. We have to treat them with respect and courtesy. We have to recognize that sometimes they are sexual with us and at other times they are not – and that is their choice.

But what goes on in your head when masturbating is very revealing of how these two contrary images of women have taken hold and become planted in your sub-consciousness.

For tantric sex to work well we have to adjust our view of women and their sexuality. We have to accord them the right respect and the right degree of independence. We cannot use them as mere outlets for our own desires and needs and wants.

Practical assignment: Self-loving 2

Go through the same process as you did in the last assignment, but this time concentrate on your feelings towards your own body. Again, use a blindfold to isolate yourself within the confines of your own mind. Before you begin to masturbate, allow yourself to touch all the parts of your body. Which bits feel right to touch? Which bits feel wrong? Are there areas you want to touch more or would want your partner to touch more when you are making love? Have you communicated this to her?

As you begin to masturbate use the fingers of your other hand to explore the inside of your thighs and buttocks and perineum (the line of skin that links the testes with the anus) and feel the exquisite pleasure there.

Take time to explore the feelings in your penis. Alter your rhythm. Alter the style and strength of your stroke. Spend time massaging your penis rather than masturbating it. This exercise is designed to get you comfortable with your own body and sexuality without having to perform for someone else. Here you are alone and you can do anything with yourself that you want to. What are you going to do? How will you pleasure yourself? Do you know what you like and want sexually?

Take time to build up to orgasm. This isn't a race against the clock. There are no prizes for coming quickly. Your time is your own and if you are enjoying doing what you are doing, why rush?

As you orgasm feel the various stages – see the section opposite for the various stages of arousal and orgasm – and experience the feelings 'behind' the orgasm as a spiritual exercise.

What is real sex?

Of course many men will already feel easy with themselves and doing these exercises may seem like going back to basics that are unnecessary. But as soon as we question the validity of these exercises we are questioning whether or not we want to spend time self-pleasuring. If we do question this, then what else do we think we ought to be doing that would be more beneficial? This throws up interesting ideas about what sort of sex is 'right' or good. For a lot of men, masturbation seems like a starter and only 'real' sex is worthy of them. For others, masturbation is fine, it holds no terrors, but 'real' sex is scary. Self-loving exercises are designed to make you commit to yourself. Masturbation is no 'better' or 'worse' than 'real' sex

– merely different. Once we are comfortable with ourselves we might be more comfortable with our partner – and with her sexuality. If we can't be completely open and relaxed with ourselves, how are we ever going to be so with another person? If we don't fully know what we like and want sexually how can we ever communicate our wants and needs to our partner?

Knowing what is happening

Knowing what is happening to you during sex is important – you need to know how close to orgasm you are at times and it is vital to be able to recognize the signs. There are four distinct phases to orgasm:

- **excitement** – penile erection, thickening, flattening and elevation of the scrotal sac, partial testicular elevation and an increase in size
- **plateau** – increase in penile circumference, testicular tumescence, change in hue of penis head to deep purple, secretion from Cowper's gland (pre-come)
- **orgasmic phase** – ejaculation accompanied by contractions of vas deferens, seminal vesicles, prostate and ejaculatory duct, contractions of penile urethra at 0.8 seconds for three to four contractions followed by a further two to four more anal sphincter contractions
- **resolution** – loss of penile erection.

A man will experience much more throughout his entire body than these physical reactions in his reproductive system, including erect nipples, facial flushing, hypertension, tachycardia and sweating. His emotional and spiritual response can also be intense.

Practical assignment: Excitement and plateau

As in the last two practical assignments, you need to be private and have lots of time. If you find these exercises easier naked, then that's fine. Lie down comfortably and use the blindfold – again to shut out senses and to isolate yourself so you can concentrate more easily on your inner sensations.

Begin by caressing yourself gently – inside of thighs, buttocks, the perineum, testes and penis. Using oil can make this experience more erotic and sensuous. As you caress yourself be aware that you are entering the excitement stage. You will feel the blood coursing through you and filling your penis. As you get excited and have an erection you can begin to masturbate, but this time you don't want to arrive at an orgasm too quickly.

Take time caressing yourself and masturbating. Concentrate on the feelings you are experiencing in your genitals. The purpose of this practical assignment is for you to become very aware of what happens to you physically as you masturbate. Normally we want to have an orgasm – that's where the ecstasy and relief is. But this time you want to bring yourself up to the point of orgasm – and not beyond, or at least not yet – and then stop. By practising this exercise regularly over a period of time you will begin to feel the ejaculate rising and then stop. As you get more experienced you will be able to stop closer and closer to the point of orgasm. Just stopping masturbating will usually stop the ejaculate rising any further providing you stop soon enough. But sometimes you will need to practise the 'squeeze technique' outlined in the next practical assignment.

By bringing yourself closer and closer to orgasm, you will eventually enter a stage where you experience the sensation of orgasm without having an ejaculation. This is the non-ejaculatory orgasm so highly thought of in tantric sex. A word of warning though – it is very hard to achieve and will take months of regular practice.

If, initially, you do accidentally orgasm, that's fine. You haven't 'failed', merely found one of many ways that doesn't work. Leave it for a while and try again. When you do orgasm try and concentrate on what is happening within your body both physically and energy-wise. Try not to concentrate on 'having' the orgasm but on what is going on behind or underneath the orgasm. Try to feel the muscles involved in pumping the ejaculate. Try to feel the ejaculate rising. After some practice you should be able to feel the entire ejaculate journey. Once you can do this it is possible to stop it at any point along its pathway. Very experienced tantric practitioners claim to be able to stop it virtually as it explodes from the penis – and others to be able to draw it back in as it leaves. Whether these claims are true or not is an interesting research project for you in the future!

Some men find that stopping the ejaculate as it travels along is quite hard by willpower alone and that they need some other form of 'stopping' mechanism. The next practical exercise can be carried out alone or with the help of your partner. It is known as the squeeze technique for reasons that will shortly become abundantly clear. If you get your partner to help, you will need to be very clear about:

- when you want them to squeeze
- where you want them to squeeze
- how hard you want them to squeeze.

We are dealing with sensitive bits here and you shouldn't be squeezed so hard that it hurts or damage is done. It might be better to try this one alone first so you can tell exactly when and where you need the squeeze technique to take place and how much pressure to use.

Practical assignment: The squeeze technique 1

As the ejaculate begins its journey it starts off quite slowly and, as it nears the outside world, it gathers speed and force. The ejaculation itself can be explosive and dramatic. Stopping this ejaculation can be very difficult. One very good technique is the squeeze technique. To do this you need to know your own body cycles and rhythms pretty well. After doing some of the early practical assignments you should by now have a fairly good idea of the progress of the ejaculate and be able to feel it. To do this you need to concentrate on what is happening rather than on what you are experiencing.

Again, this is a masturbatory practical assignment although you can do this one with a partner if you so choose. As you masturbate feel the ejaculate begin to rise. By squeezing the perineum – the line of ridged skin between your anus and your testes – you can stop the ejaculation and it will subside. How much pressure you need to use depends on various factors:

- your excitement levels (if you are masturbating these will be lower than if you are having sex with your partner)
- how close to the ejaculation you choose to stop it
- the frequency of previous ejaculations (if you have masturbated within the previous 24 hours it will be much easier to stop)
- how aware you are of the rise of the ejaculate.

You should experiment with what sort of pressure you need and what type of pressure. For some men it is sufficient to press hard with one or two fingers, pushing into the perineum. For other men it is necessary to pinch a fold of skin between the thumb and forefinger and to squeeze this quite hard.

This squeeze technique works well if you are masturbating or having sex in such a position that you or your partner can easily reach the perineum. There is another squeeze technique that is equally as effective but is more difficult to perform while actually having sex. Nevertheless it is still one worth learning and practising.

Practical assignment: The squeeze technique 2

This technique requires a 'closer to the edge' approach – it only works immediately prior to ejaculation, whereas the previous squeeze technique works right through the rise of the ejaculate. If you masturbate until almost the very moment you are about to come and then squeeze the head of your penis very firmly between your thumb and forefinger and index finger you should, by exerting considerable force, be able to stop the ejaculate. Don't worry, there isn't a lot of damage you could do by squeezing too hard and it doesn't really hurt although I admit it might sound as if it does when you read this. Try it. It is usually sufficient to stop any ejaculation.

You can experiment with how high up the penis you squeeze and how hard. Most men find that it has to be the head of the penis that is squeezed rather than lower down as this seems less effective owing to the thickness of flesh separating your fingers and the ejaculate whereas the head of the penis is much more in contact.

Some men have reported that they can stop the ejaculate by squeezing the eye of the penis quite hard. Again you will need to experiment.

PC muscle

If you want to be good at sex – and your interest in tantric sex implies you do – then you have to do some training. If you wanted to lift huge weights in the gym, you'd start with small, light ones and work up. You wouldn't expect to lift the really big weights on your first day. It's the same with sex. You have to start small and work up. The trouble is that many people – in fact most people – start small with sex and then stay exactly there. They think they're doing it well, doing it magnificently, when in fact they're merely enjoying the very basic levels, the first beginnings of what should actually be a superb and well-orchestrated symphony. Why settle for a quick tune on a penny whistle when you could have a complete orchestra?

One of the main muscles you will need to develop if you are to move on to a symphony is the PC muscle. Its full name is the *pubococcygeus* muscle but you may hear it referred to as the *Kegel muscle* after the gynaecologist Arnold Kegel who first recommended its development and strengthening in the 1940s. His system of muscle-strengthening exercises are still known as Kegel exercises, although similar exercises have formed part of tantric training for centuries. He recommended strengthening the PC muscle as a means to improve incontinence in women that often follows childbirth. The PC muscle also facilitates orgasm in women which was found out as a sort of side-effect of improving the incontinence. The same is true for men.

So what and where is the PC muscle?

You can regard the PC muscle as the sort of throwing mechanism for the ejaculate but it also improves and strengthens the orgasm.

If a woman inserts one finger into her vagina and attempts to grip her finger it is the PC muscle she will be using. After training this muscle becomes much stronger. In men the PC muscle can first be felt if they interrupt the stream of urine. It is this muscle which stops the flow.

In both men and women the muscle is located between the legs stretching between the genitals and the anus. If you imagine you are having a bowel movement and that you've got to hold back – it's the PC muscle you are using. If men stand in front of a mirror naked they should see their penis 'twitch' as they squeeze this muscle.

Another way of testing that you've got the right muscle is to insert one well-lubricated finger into the anus and squeeze the anal walls. If you grip the finger then you've got the right muscle. Initially, pretty nearly everyone tenses too much. They involve muscles in the buttocks and thighs and even lower abdomen when they first start squeezing the PC muscle. You don't need to. The squeeze is very localized and it should only be necessary to tension the PC muscle on its own.

Once you have found the PC muscle and correctly identified it and how to squeeze it you should begin by doing a few contractions every day. Ideally, you need to do three sessions a day with around 20 contractions per session – the biggest problem is simply remembering to do your PC exercises.

After a couple of weeks increase the 20 a session to 50 a session – thus 150 a day. And after another couple of weeks increase to 100 per session – thus 300 a day. These figures are an ideal and it is appreciated that not everyone will achieve this. Even doing ten a session is better than nothing. Just so long as you completely relax between contractions. If you don't then you won't gain a lot of benefit. Relaxing between contractions is essential if you want to strengthen this muscle.

When to do the PC exercises

Anytime, any place, anywhere. Yep, it is possible to be holding a conversation with a complete stranger and still doing your PC exercises – they'll never know. No one will. What is going on is completely internal, completely hidden. You might find them easier to do, initially, if you are sitting down. Standing up is slightly harder but probably more effective as it requires very dedicated focusing on the PC muscle to stop you tensing everything else.

Basically what you are doing is encouraging this muscle to grow. Like any muscle, if you use it then it gets bigger, stronger and more able to do its job efficiently.

Practical assignment: PC muscle breathing

Find somewhere comfortable to sit down where you can relax and not be disturbed. Sitting on a hard, straight-backed chair is best rather than a squishy sofa. Close your eyes and begin a rhythmic contraction of the PC muscle. As you clench it breathe in deeply using your lower abdomen. As you relax the muscle breathe out and relax your entire body.

Try to imagine the breath that you are breathing in is actually entering your body through your anus rather than your nose. As you breathe imagine the muscle as a spiral of coiled energy growing stronger – like a spring of steel.

This breathing assignment is linked to others we will do shortly and it helps to remember this as PC breathing so that later, when you read 'do this in conjunction with PC breathing', you'll know what to do.

Keeping it up

Once you have begun to develop the PC muscle – and this will take, on average, around two months – you will begin to feel the benefits. As you ejaculate begin a series of very fast contractions and relaxations of the PC muscle – you'll find you come hard, stronger, longer and more intensely than ever before. You will literally be using the PC muscle exactly as it is intended to be used – as a pump. Most men, when they ejaculate, are victims of an involuntary response, but men who have developed their PC muscle are in control. They take responsibility for their orgasm with a sense of strength and direction. They are choosing when and how to ejaculate. That must be much better than merely poking and squirting.

If you are making love and feel you are about to ejaculate and don't want to (for example, if you want to continue for longer to aid your partner's pleasure) then just squeeze the PC muscle as hard as you can – and hold it there. This intense squeeze is often enough to stop the ejaculation as long as you catch it early enough. Men who have spent several years developing their PC muscle will be able to time this intense contraction to the very nano second and stop the ejaculation almost as it is on the point of bursting forth from the penis, but this does require intense and long training.

Doing any PC exercises will bring benefits. You will increase bloodflow and circulation to the entire genital/anal region which is good for your whole sexual response. You will learn control and be in charge. You will learn to focus on your sexual organs which is an essential for tantric training.

Remembering to do your PC exercises is important. Remembering to use your PC muscle as a spiritual energy pump is also important – but much harder to remember. Once you find yourself in the throes of an orgasm it is obviously hard to remember to do something else as well as enjoying your orgasm, but if you do remember you will be rewarded. If you remember to pump as you come it is pretty well guaranteed that you will have the most intense orgasm you have ever experienced – each and every time. Once you have experienced the PC pumping orgasm you will find it much easier to remember – pleasure is a great incentive. But it is more than mere pleasure. The intensity of the orgasm when you use the PC muscle as a pump is also accompanied by a great rush of spiritual energy that lifts the orgasm from the mere physical to something quite sublime. You experience something of the godhead. Once you have experienced this over a period it gets easier to keep pumping even as your orgasm subsides and, as you do so, you'll feel the energy rising throughout your body. Eventually, if you do this often enough and vigorously enough, you will be rewarded by the energy reaching the top of your head – the great reunion of God and Goddess. This is the *kundalini* energy being completely released to flood out into the universe.

Improving energy techniques

We have already looked at ways of improving our physical performance by delaying ejaculation so we can make love for longer and better. But there are also ways of improving the way our sexual energy flows and this next section is all about developing our energy performance.

If we extrapolate information about the way energy – especially sexual energy – is supposed to move, in the male body, from various tantric traditions including Taoist and Hindu we can get a pretty good idea of how to improve it. Sexual energy in men lies dormant in their base chakra. There are seven energy centres located in the main trunk of the body and the base chakra is the one concerned with our basic identity, our genetic beginnings. The base chakra is located just inside the male body lying slightly inside the area of the perineum. If you push hard on this area you are stimulating the base chakra. In men, the sexual energy lies dormant here until aroused by sexual activity. If men are in the heightened throes of an orgasm this energy will uncoil sufficiently to perhaps reach their second chakra – the pelvic or sex chakra. It is worth having a quick look in more detail at the seven chakras.

- **The base chakra** – *muladhara* – situated at the base of the spine between the genitals and the anus. This chakra governs our instincts and genetic coding. It is usually represented by a yellow square. The mantra for the base chakra is *lam*.
- **The pelvic chakra** – *swadhishthana* – situated at the genitals themselves. This chakra governs our sexual life. It is usually represented by a white crescent. The mantra for the pelvis chakra is *vam*.
- **The navel chakra** – *manipuraka* – situated at the navel. This chakra governs our personal power. It is usually represented by a red triangle. The mantra for the navel chakra is *ram*.

- **The heart chakra** – *anahata* – situated at the heart. This chakra governs our love. It is usually represented by a blue hexagon. The mantra for the heart chakra is *yam*.
- **The throat chakra** – *vishuddha* – situated at the throat. This chakra governs our communication. It is usually represented by a white circle. The mantra for the throat chakra is *ham*.
- **The brow chakra** – *ajna* – situated between the brows. This chakra governs our intellect and thought processes. It is usually represented by an inverted white triangle. The mantra for the brow chakra is *om*.
- **The crown chakra** – *sahasrara* – situated at the crown of the head. This is not a true chakra like the others, but rather is known as a *shuddha* because it doesn't operate in quite the same way as the others. It is the home of the Goddess Shakti – the God Shiva is said to reside in the brow chakra. The whole point of raising the *kundalini* energy from the base chakra up the spine to the brow chakra and then on the crown chakra, is to free Shiva so he may be reunited with Shakti and the great cosmic reunion of the male and female principles can take place. This state of divine bliss is known as *samadhi* – enlightenment.

Each of these chakras also has a Hindu god attributed to it as well as various symbolic animals, flowers, elements, seasons and a letter of the Sanskrit alphabet. A detailed study of the chakras would more than fill this book. We need only be concerned with the basics here.

Practical assignment: Chakra meditation

You should lie down somewhere warm and comfortable. Imagine the site of each chakra as a small, tightly-furled flower or small leather bag. As you breathe out make the mantra sound for each chakra as you visualize it in turn, starting with the base chakra and finishing with the brow chakra. Imagine each chakra as a flower opening as you breathe out – or the small leather bag having draw strings which are being slowly loosened.

Work your way up the body imagining each chakra opening as you make the mantra sound as you exhale. You need to do this exercise with your eyes closed so you can visualise each chakra in turn. This exercise can be done before you make love with your partner so that you are fully open and ready to feel energy moving within your body.

Once you've begun to feel the chakras you can move on to exploring the way your sexual energy can move up through the chakras to the crown – the rising of the *kundalini* energy.

Practical assignment: Chakra meditation with kundalini energy

Again make sure you can't be disturbed and lie down on the floor. Be warm and comfortable. Put a blanket underneath you. If you feel better being naked then that's fine. Raise your knees and keep your feet flat on the floor. Put your hands flat across your belly. Lift your pelvis and begin to slowly rock it from side to side. You are awakening the energy. You can rock as fast as you want but always start off slowly.

As you rock begin your PC breathing. Time your swings to coincide with your breaths – rock from each side and exhale, rock again and inhale as you do so.

As you breathe in imagine cosmic fire being drawn into your anus with the breath. This is the base *kundalini* energy that you are going to transform, through tantra, to the highest *kundalini* energy that will explode from your crown chakra.

As you draw in the fiery *kundalini* energy see it as a dark, blood-red fire, sluggish, hot, deep, all-burning, all-powerful, sleepy heat. Imagine this blood-red fluid being transformed to a lighter red as it reaches the second chakra – the *swadhishthana* – located at the genitals. Then imagine the fire travelling to the third chakra at the navel – the *manipuraka* – and getting lighter still, an orangey yellow. On to the next chakra located at the heart – *anahata* – and turning into a stronger yellow with tints of green as if copper were being burnt in it. Then on to the throat chakra – the *vishuddha* – and turning blue, the blue flames of truth and purity. Then up to the brow chakra – the *ajna* – and the flames turning bluish-purple, mauve, pale violet. And finally imagine the flames reaching the crown chakra and turning completely white – the *sahasrara*. Imagine the flames losing their heat and becoming watery, liquid. Imagine this liquid, this cosmic water, spraying out of the top of your head like semen fertilizing the entire universe.

Keep rocking as you do this practical assignment as this rocking is the pump that will move this *kundalini* energy up your entire body.

The way energy moves

For men and women the energy moves differently. The man will feel this energy slowly working its way up his spine, while for the woman the energy will rise slowly up through the belly first and then the breasts. The man's energy, being hotter and more volatile, may well rise faster but he should not rush it. The woman's energy, being cooler and slower to arouse, will take longer. If during any exercise either becomes aroused to the point of orgasm then that's all right. Because we are orgasm oriented in the West it may take a while to learn to focus on the energy rather than the sexual experience. Whatever way you do it, it should be an enjoyable experience.

The approach of delight

The whole basis of raising the *kundalini* energy is to share and experience the 'godhead' – if this isn't done in a spirit of delight and enjoyment it will not be successful. There are some who have spent a whole lifetime practising tantric sex and getting nowhere because they do the whole thing as a ritual and miss the point completely.

You have to enter into tantric sex with an approach of delight – what happens is happening and it's all right. Sometimes there will be a union of soul with soul and sometimes not – but the journey should be enjoyed without thought of the destination, or the experience that is presented along the way will be lost.

If, during any practical assignment, you become aroused – enjoy it. And there should be no spiritual ego to taunt your partner with – 'Oh, I attained enlightenment and all you achieved was orgasm.'

Reunion with God

Use the experience as it comes and try to use the energy in a beneficial way. The principle aim or objective of raising the *kundalini* energy is to reunite or connect with the energy of the universe through the unique and wonderful experience of sex – tantra is a reunion with God.

Appreciating

During any exercise the energy may become very sleepy – go with it and use the time given as a meditation. Focus on the brow chakra (see page 55) and allow yourself to appreciate what you can see, feel and hear. There is a reason, according to the tantric Buddhists, why the energy can take any one of many different forms. It may be orgasmic, meditative or spiritually enlightening – it may even be all three – but the energy generated is being transformed into exactly what you need at any given moment. It may not be what you expect – or even what you particularly want – but it will be what you need. The tantric Buddhists recommend that you go with it – if you don't fight the universe it will provide you with everything you need.

Practical assignment: Being in touch with your body

This exercise will also put you in touch with your genital feelings. We focus on our genitals usually only in the rush of orgasm or if they are being caressed. During this exercise you can focus on your genitals. How do they feel? Wholesome and healthy? Or is there some residual guilt or inhibition there? According to the tantric Buddhists one of the reasons we sometimes fail to achieve a truly deep spiritual/sexual experience is because we are somehow hanging onto our fears and repression. During this exercise you can explore your feelings about your sexuality – and your body as a sexual instrument.

With your left hand hold your penis and scrotum. Place your fingers under the scrotum with your thumb pressing into your pubic region. This works best if you don't have an erection.

Place your right hand on your navel and begin to slowly circle your stomach as in the old patting your head while rubbing your tummy routine. Only this time instead of patting your head hold your sex organs lovingly. Do some 100 circles anti-clockwise. As you do this breathe deeply, close your eyes and focus on your genitals. What do you feel there? You are rubbing the energy into life at the solar plexus and you should begin to feel warmth and life there.

All the chakras are linked to major glandular centres in the body which shows the ancient Hindus knew their stuff. By doing the chakra meditations you are also stimulating the glandular centres. For instance, concentrating on your third eye – the brow chakra – will stimulate the pineal gland which has been referred to as 'the happiness gland'. Stimulate it and you increase your contentment levels. The same goes for the base chakra – stimulate it and you stimulate the prostate gland.

Storing energy

Tantra recommends and suggests that sexual energy be 'stored'. You can raise it and store it in what is known as the *hara*. This is a Japanese word meaning belly and that is exactly where we are going to store the male sexual energy – in your belly.

Practical assignment: Storing energy

Find somewhere where you won't be disturbed and can feel safe and relaxed. Be naked for this practical assignment. Sit cross-legged on the floor with your hands lightly resting on your knees. Begin by PC breathing. As you pump the PC muscle imagine it pumping energy into your belly. As you relax imagine the pump shutting off so that the energy remains in your belly and with each new contraction you pump more energy in. Focus on your belly and feel the warmth of the energy there. Men's energy is hot and vital and you should feel considerable heat being accumulated. Allow this warmth to spread out through your whole body. You are becoming a total sexual being – hot, vital, energetic, primed. You can imagine your entire body as a huge penis. Your head is the head of the penis and the *hara* is your testicles with all their energy latent and stored.

Keep breathing. Keep focused. Imagine this energy rising up from your *hara* to the top of your head. Imagine it spurting out into the universe. This is the *kundalini* energy rising up and being reunited with the universe which is where it came from. You are making love with the entire cosmos. Now imagine you are making love with your partner. Imagine the massive power you now contain, sexually. What sort of lovemaking could you achieve now?

Understanding energy

If you have never meditated or carried out any form of spiritual exercise some of this talk of inner energy may leave you confused and apprehensive. There is no need to be so but it is understandable if you have never experienced any form of inner contemplation.

Experiencing inner energy is easy if you are prepared to devote a few minutes each day. You need to learn a basic meditation so you, too, can journey inwards to experience something of what is happening within you.

So we've considered performance enhancing techniques and techniques to experience the movement of internal energy. You are now ready for the next step – putting all this into practice with your lover and partner. Before you do this it is worth reading the chapter on practical assignments for women so you know what she is studying and enhancing. There will be considerable opportunity to do these things together and you really do need to know and understand how a woman's energy moves and how different it is from your own.

Summary

In this chapter we have looked a lots of ways for men to get closer in touch with their sexuality – privately and alone. Not only have we covered the practical assignments to put you in touch with your own 'performance' techniques but also to enhance your spirituality.

We have also looked at the four stages of sexual excitement, arousal and orgasm: excitement, plateau, orgasmic phase and resolution. It is important to know and understand what is happening throughout our bodies during sex so we are better able to control and improve our sexual performance.

We have looked at ways of controlling – and stopping – ejaculation, so we are better able to control our orgasms. This enables us to give our partner more pleasure as well as enabling us to gain more control over our own performance.

We have explored our PC (pubococcygeus) muscle and have done some exercises to strengthen and improve this. This PC muscle, when developed, enables is to have longer, stronger and better orgasms. And once we have begun to develop this muscle we can begin to use PC muscle breathing – using the muscle at the point of ejaculation and exploring the spiritual side of our orgasm.

We looked at the seven chakras and what each means and how to begin to experience them. We also considered the way energy moves in our body, what that energy does and how we can improve its flow.

06
practical assignments for women

In this chapter you will learn:
- about building tension
- about the approach of delight
- how to release energy for women.

There is a childlike quality and simplicity to so many of the Taoist practices.

Eric Steven Yudelove, *Taoist Yoga and Sexual Energy*

Obviously there is a vast overlap in the information about how sexual energy moves for men and women. If you haven't read the previous chapter, assuming it is all for men and thus nothing to do with you, then I recommend you turn back and read it. It is essential for you to know what is happening for your partner. You need to know, as they need to know about you, so you can be supportive in their practical assignments. Respect each other's privacy. There is plenty of scope for both of you to practise together following the practical assignments for couples in Chapter 08.

So, this is your turn, your practical assignments, your chance to understand and use the tantric energy. It will be necessary to repeat a lot of the information in the previous chapter so that you don't have to keep turning back to read what has been previously explained.

Women who participate in tantric sex practices become alive, vibrant, vital, orgasmic and powerful. There is no place for girls here – this is for the Goddess. You will learn to be in control, in charge, forceful and dynamic. Are you ready for all this? Are you ready to seize control of your sexuality and become sexually alive? Good. In this chapter we will learn:

• performance techniques to enhance both the strength and duration of your orgasms
• performance techniques to enhance the frequency and number of your orgasms
• how to enjoy different types of orgasm
• energy techniques to enhance internal energy movements
• spirituality techniques to put you in touch with an inner experience.

In this chapter you will find a lot of practical assignments to improve your sexual techniques, but before we do that we need to improve the biggest sexual organ you have – your mind. In order to improve it we need to find out where you are in relation to your sexuality. How open are you? How relaxed about your sexuality are you? How sexually free are you? There is only one way to find out – by experimentation. This first practical assignment for you is not a test or an exam. It is just a way of monitoring – for yourself alone – how you feel about sex and your own sexuality and that of your partner.

Practical assignment: Self-loving 1

For this assignment all you need is yourself and a blindfold. Be alone in a warm room where you feel private and safe and aren't going to be interrupted. This practical assignment is best done in the evening when your *ch'i* energy is still and you are rested. Don't do this exercise on a full stomach, so only eat a light supper. Lie down in a comfortable position. You will need to be naked and feel easy with yourself. You are going to masturbate yourself to orgasm. We aren't interested in what happens in and to your body. Instead what we want to concentrate on is what goes on inside your head while you are pleasuring yourself.

Follow your thoughts. The idea behind the blindfold is both practical – to stop you seeing – and symbolic – to isolate you within the confines of your own mind. As you masturbate, what images do you call to mind? Do you see yourself in erotic, loving situations or abusive degrading ones? Do you see yourself as powerful and in control or as a passive non-participant?

As you achieve orgasm, what goes through your mind? Are you alone or with a partner? If you are with a partner (male or female) do they have a face? Do you feel love? How do you see your partner/lover in your mind as you climax?

This is a practical assignment to get you thinking about how you view sex and men, your sexuality and your partner's. It isn't intended to be a judgement or a criticism. It is merely a way of discovering the truth within each of us.

Women grow up with conflicting ideas about sex as men do. For you it may well be that you were encouraged to think of sex as something 'nice girls don't do' or that it was dirty or sinful. But as you grow into womanhood you have pleasurable feelings which need exploring. By masturbating are you being dirty and/or sinful? Or just sexually open and grown up? Women are given to believe that their sexuality is a precious gift and that men have to earn the right to it. But, at the same time, they are led to believe that sex is forbidden and something to be kept secret. So how do you feel?

By following the practical assignments in this chapter you can learn to explore your sexuality and be open and honest both with yourself and your partner. If you have a bad self-image or feel in any way lacking in sexual self-esteem, tantric practices will help you overcome these negative images. By learning to love yourself, as a woman, you will be able to give of yourself more freely and to use your sexuality creatively and passionately.

Practical assignment: Self-loving 2

Go through the same process as you did in the last assignment, but this time concentrate on your feelings towards your own body. Again, use a blindfold to isolate yourself within the confines of your own mind. Before you begin to masturbate, allow yourself to touch all the parts of your body. Which bits feel right to touch? Which bits feel wrong? Are there areas you want to touch more or would want your partner to touch more when you are making love? Have you communicated this to him?

As you begin to masturbate use the fingers of your other hand to explore the inside of your thighs and buttocks and perineum (the line of skin that links the vagina with the anus) and feel the exquisite pleasure there. Stroke your breasts and feel how your nipples harden as you get excited.

Take time to explore the feelings in your clitoris and vagina. Alter your rhythm. Alter the style and strength of your caress. Spend time massaging your clitoris rather than masturbating it. This exercise is designed to get you comfortable with your own body and sexuality without having to perform for someone else. Here you are alone and you can do anything with yourself that you want to. What are you going to do? How will you pleasure yourself? Do you know what you like and want sexually?

Take time to build up to orgasm. This isn't a race against the clock. There are no prizes for coming quickly. Your time is your own and if you are enjoying doing what you are doing, why rush?

As you orgasm feel the various stages – see page 66 for the various stages of arousal and orgasm – and experience the feelings 'behind' the orgasm as a spiritual exercise.

For a lot of women there will be mixed feelings about masturbation and likewise about 'real' sex. Women know what they want and need to achieve orgasm, but being with a man often causes them to 'clam up' and somehow they don't communicate what it is they need. The consequence of this is that they are left feeling unsatisfied – especially if their lover isn't expert or experienced. Sex becomes a disappointment instead of a wonderfully expressive act of spiritual and physical regeneration. Part of tantric sex is being assertive and learning good communication. The next practical assignment may help you with this.

Practical assignment: Assertive self-loving

Again, as in the previous exercise, be comfortable and safe – there should be no interruptions. It is best to do this exercise alone initially, but later you can do it for the benefit of your partner if you wish.

You are going to masturbate as before but this time you are going to talk yourself through the process loudly and very verbally. As you masturbate, express what it is you are doing: 'Now I am stroking my nipples, not too hard but quite firmly. I am licking my fingers to wet my clitoris as when it is dry it doesn't feel so good. I am sliding one finger inside my vagina as I rub my clitoris. I am rubbing faster now as I can feel myself starting to come. As I come I am pulling very hard on my nipples as I like this but can only stand this level of hardness when I am coming and not at any other time. As I come I stop rubbing completely and withdraw my finger as I like to lie completely still now. After a minute or two, when I have got my breath back, I can start caressing myself again and make myself come again. I need to make myself come at least x times to feel completely satisfied.'

For each of you what you say will be different. For each of you there will be a series of manoeuvres you need to go through to achieve orgasm. This practical assignment is useful for learning how to verbalize what it is you need and want. How can your partner know if you don't tell him? How can he learn if you don't teach him? And you can only teach him if you are prepared to tell him what it is you want him to do – how hard, how long, how gentle, how vigorous, how loving, how moist. Try to see your role as that of teacher as well as sexual partner. Men need to be told. Men need you to verbalize your wants as they may not be too good at picking up subtle signals. This may be a sweeping generalization but it is probably true of most men. They need direct instruction. This can only benefit you.

Knowing what is happening

Sex is an intricate business – a skill that has to be learnt. For so many of us it is something we 'pick up as we go along'. Not many of us take the time and trouble to read up on the subject or to study it in any depth, but we all expect to be good at it without effort. Unfortunately, this simply doesn't work. In order to enhance our orgasms we have to know what is happening before, during and after. There are four distinct phases to orgasm:

- **excitement** – vaginal lubrication, a thickening of the vaginal walls and labia, swelling or enlargement of the clitoris, erection of the nipples
- **plateau** – expansion of the vagina, colouring of the labia, withdrawal of the clitoris, secretions from Bartholin's gland – pre-come
- **orgasmic phase** – contractions at the rate of approximately 0.8 seconds for between 5 and 12 contractions followed by a further 3 to 6, contractions of the sphincter and urethra
- **resolution** – return of normal colouration to labia, tumescence of clitoris returns to normal position, vagina size decreases.

These are the four distinct phases, but obviously they may not be that distinct when you are in the throes of your orgasms – the lines do get blurred. For example, you don't go from the excitement phase straight to the orgasmic stage without first going through the plateau, although you may not realize it at the time as the transition from one phase to the next may be smooth and seamless. Neither are you likely to go from plateau to resolution without going through the orgasmic stage – you can't miss out stages.

During these phases there is so much more going on than this. You will also experience such things as:

- facial flushing
- hypertension
- tachycardia (speeded-up heart rate)
- sweating
- contractions of the sphincter.

As well as the physiological changes there will be intense emotional and spiritual ones as well.

Building tension

In tantric sex there is a great emphasis placed on the tension that leads up to orgasm – the plateau phase. For men this is a very important part of tantric training as it teaches them how to stop their ejaculation so they can rise higher and higher at the plateau stage to have a deeper and more intense orgasm – or even multiple orgasms – without ejaculation. For women there is a capacity to have multiple orgasms as well. But for some women this isn't their experience so they too need to learn how to use the plateau phase to springboard themselves to a more enhanced orgasm. The next practical assignment is for women who orgasm too easily or who don't have multiple orgasms.

Practical assignment: Excitement and plateau

As in the last two practical assignments, you need to be private and have lots of time. If you find these exercises easier naked then that's fine. Lie down comfortably and use the blindfold – again to shut out senses and to isolate yourself so you can concentrate more easily on your inner sensations.

Begin by caressing yourself gently – inside of thighs, buttocks, the perineum, labia and clitoris. Using oil can make this experience more erotic and sensuous. As you caress yourself be aware that you are entering the excitement stage. You will feel the blood coursing through you and filling your vagina. As you get excited and feel the vagina swelling you can begin to masturbate, but this time you don't want to arrive at an orgasm too quickly.

Take time caressing yourself and masturbating. Concentrate on the feelings you are experiencing in your vagina. The purpose of this practical assignment is for you to become very aware of what happens to you physically as you masturbate. Normally we want to have an orgasm – that's where the pleasure is. But this time you want to bring yourself up to the point of orgasm – and not beyond, or at least not yet – and then stop. By practising this exercise regularly over a period of time you will begin to feel the orgasm mounting and then stop. As you get more experienced you will be able to stop closer and closer to the point of orgasm. Just stopping masturbating will usually stop the orgasm escalating any further, providing you stop soon enough. You should see the excitement as something that can be intensified by bringing it up to a peak, stopping and then taking it higher without having the orgasm. As you practise you will find that when you finally do choose to have your orgasm it will be very intense indeed and quite likely to spill over into several orgasms – the multiple orgasm.

This is a very good exercise for learning control – you choose when you are going to have your orgasm rather than its happening by chance so to speak. You become very powerful when you have this control as well as experiencing greater and more intense orgasms.

PC muscle

If you want to be good at sex – and your interest in tantric sex implies you do – then you have to do some training. If you want to get from A to B it pays to learn to drive. So you take lessons. You don't sit in the car and try and figure out how the controls work all by yourself. And getting from A to B is so much easier in a car. Why settle for riding a bike when you could be swishing along in a Jaguar?

One of the main muscles you will need to develop if you are to study sex for real is the PC muscle. Its full name is the *pubococcygeus* muscle but you may hear it referred to as the *Kegel muscle* after the gynaecologist Arnold Kegel who first recommended its development and strengthening in the 1940s. His system of muscle-strengthening exercises are still known as Kegel exercises, although similar exercises have formed part of tantric training for centuries. He recommended strengthening the PC muscle as a means to improve incontinence in women that often follows childbirth. The PC muscle also facilitates orgasm in women which was found out as a sort of side-effect of improving the incontinence.

So what and where is the PC muscle?

If you insert one finger into your vagina and attempt to grip your finger it is the PC muscle you are using. After training this muscle becomes much stronger. You can also locate it by urinating and stopping the flow in mid-stream. It is the PC muscle which does the 'stopping'.

In both men and women the muscle is located between the legs stretching between the genitals and the anus. If you imagine you are having a bowel movement and that you've got to hold back – it's the PC muscle you are using.

Another way of testing that you've got the right muscle is to insert one well-lubricated finger into the anus and squeeze the anal walls. If you grip the finger then you've got the right muscle. Initially pretty nearly everyone tenses too much. They involve muscles in the buttocks and thighs and even lower abdomen when they first start squeezing the PC muscle. You don't need to. The squeeze is very localized and it should only be necessary to tension the PC muscle on its own.

Once you have found the PC muscle and correctly identified it and how to squeeze it you should begin by doing a few contractions every day. Ideally you need to do three sessions a day with around 20 contractions a session. Building up to 60 contractions a day will take a few days – the biggest problem is simply remembering to do your PC exercises.

After a couple of weeks increase the 20 a session to 50 – thus 150 a day. And after another couple of weeks increase to 100 per session – thus 300 a day. These figures are an ideal and it is appreciated that not everyone will achieve this. Even doing ten a session is better than nothing. Just so long as you completely relax between contractions. If you don't then you won't gain a lot of benefit. Relaxing between contractions is essential if you want to strengthen this muscle.

When to do the PC exercises

Anytime, any place, anywhere. It is possible to be holding a conversation with a complete stranger and still doing your PC exercises – they'll never know. No one will. What is going on is completely internal, completely hidden. You might find them easier to do, initially, if you are sitting down. Standing up is slightly harder but probably more effective as it requires very dedicated focusing on the PC muscle to stop you tensing everything else.

Basically what you are doing is encouraging this muscle to grow. Like any muscle, if you use it then it gets bigger, stronger and more able to do its job efficiently.

Practical assignment: PC muscle breathing

Find somewhere comfortable to sit down where you can relax and not be disturbed. Sitting on a hard, straight-backed chair is best rather than a squishy sofa. Close your eyes and begin a rhythmic contraction of the PC muscle – really feel your vaginal walls contract vigorously – and then let go completely so you relax the muscle. As you clench it breathe in deeply using your lower abdomen. As you relax the muscle, breathe out and relax your entire body.

Try to imagine the breath that you are breathing in is actually entering your body through your anus rather than your nose. As you breathe imagine the muscle as a spiral of coiled energy growing stronger – like a spring of steel.

This assignment is linked to others we will do shortly and it helps to remember this as PC breathing so that later, when you read 'do this in conjunction with PC breathing', you'll know what to do.

Keeping it up

Obviously, you should be doing you PC muscle exercises every day but there is another way of keeping it up – using your partner's penis as a handy tool to aid you. Once he has inserted his penis into your vagina, he should stay still and let you do all the work. By rhythmic contractions of the PC muscle you can send ripples of pleasure along your vaginal walls and 'milk' his penis. You can both lie still and be apparently doing nothing, but by clenching and unclenching your PC muscle you can make both of you come.

It is said that there are some women who have developed their PC muscle to such an extent that they can stop their partner's ejaculation merely by squeezing their PC muscle very hard. This may be an ultimate goal to work towards, but for now just concentrate on doing the exercises and developing the muscle to the degree where you can feel it working, gripping and contracting at will.

When you are in the throes of an orgasm if you pump your PC muscle you will find that your orgasm will be much more intense and last longer. Pumping also seems to delay the resolution phase of orgasm so you are much more likely to orgasm again and are much more ready to enjoy further bouts of lovemaking. The intensity of the orgasm when you use the PC muscle as a pump is also accompanied by a great rush of spiritual energy that lifts the orgasm from the mere physical to something quite sublime. You experience something of the godhead. Once you have experienced this over a period it gets easier to keep pumping even as your orgasm subsides and, as you do so, you'll feel the energy rising throughout your body. Eventually, if you do this often enough and vigorously enough, you will be rewarded by the energy reaching the top of your head – the great reunion of God and Goddess. This is the *kundalini* energy being completely released to flood out into the universe.

Improving energy techniques

We have already looked at ways of improving our physical performance by strengthening and enhancing orgasms so we can make love for longer and better, but there are also ways of improving the way our sexual energy flows and this next section is all about developing our energy performance.

If we explore information about the way energy – especially sexual energy – is supposed to move, in the female body, from various tantric traditions including Taoist and Hindu we can get a pretty good idea of how to improve it. Sexual energy in women lies hidden in their base chakra. There are seven energy centres located in the main trunk of the body and the base chakra is the one concerned with our basic identity, our genetic beginnings. The base chakra is located just inside the female body lying slightly inside the area of the perineum. If you push hard on this area you are stimulating the base chakra. In women, the sexual energy lies resting here until aroused by sexual activity. If women are in the heightened throes of an orgasm this energy will uncoil sufficiently to perhaps reach their second chakra – the pelvic or sex chakra. Perhaps it is worth having a quick look in more detail at the seven chakras.

- **The base chakra** – *muladhara* – situated at the base of the spine between the genitals and the anus. This chakra governs our instincts and genetic coding. It is usually represented by a yellow square. The mantra for the base chakra is *lam*.
- **The pelvic chakra** – *swadhishthana* – situated at the genitals themselves. This chakra governs our sexual life. It is usually represented by a white crescent. The mantra for the pelvis chakra is *vam*.
- **The navel chakra** – *manipuraka* – situated at the navel. This chakra governs our personal power. It is usually represented by a red triangle. The mantra for the navel chakra is *ram*.
- **The heart chakra** – *anahata* – situated at the heart. This chakra governs our love. It is usually represented by a blue hexagon. The mantra for the heart chakra is yam.
- **The throat chakra** – *vishuddha* – situated at the throat. This chakra governs our communication. It is usually represented by a white circle. The mantra for the throat chakra is *ham*.
- **The brow chakra** – *ajna* – situated between the brows. This chakra governs our intellect and thought processes. It is usually represented by an inverted white triangle. The mantra for the brow chakra is *om*.
- **The crown chakra** – *sahasrara* – situated at the crown of the head. This is not a true chakra like the others but rather is known as a *shuddha* and it is situated at the crown of the head. It is sometimes known as the crown chakra but it doesn't operate in quite the same way as the others. It is the home of the Goddess Shakti – the God Shiva is said to reside in the brow chakra. The whole point of raising the *kundalini*

energy from the base chakra up the spine to the brow chakra, and then on the crown chakra, is to free Shiva so he may be reunited with Shakti and the great cosmic reunion of the male and female principles can take place. This state of divine bliss is known as *samadhi* – enlightenment.

Each of these chakras also has a Hindu god attributed to it as well as various symbolic animals, flowers, elements, seasons and a letter of the Sanskrit alphabet. A detailed study of the chakras could be made by the serious student that would more than fill this book. We need only be concerned with the basics here.

Practical assignment: Chakra meditation

You should lie down somewhere warm and comfortable. Imagine the site of each chakra as a small tightly-furled flower or small leather bag. As you breathe out make the mantra sound for each chakra as you visualise it in turn, starting with the base chakra and finishing with the brow chakra. Imagine each chakra as a flower opening as you breathe out – or the small leather bag having draw strings which are being slowly loosened.

Work your way up the body imagining each chakra opening as you make the mantra sound as you exhale. You need to do this exercise with your eyes closed so you can visualise each chakra in turn. This exercise can be done before you make love with your partner so that you are fully open and ready to feel energy moving within your body.

Once you've begun to feel the chakras you can move on to exploring the way your sexual energy can move up through the chakras to the crown – the rising of the *kundalini* energy.

Practical assignment: Chakra meditation with kundalini energy

Again make sure you can't be disturbed and lie down on the floor. Be warm and comfortable. Put a blanket underneath you. If you feel better being naked then that's fine. Raise your knees and keep your feet flat on the floor. Put your hands flat across your belly. Lift your pelvis and begin slowly to rock it from side to side. You are awakening the energy. You can rock as fast as you want but always start off slowly.

As you rock begin your PC breathing. Time your swings to coincide with your breaths – rock from each side and exhale, rock again and inhale as you do so.

As you breathe in, imagine cosmic fire being drawn into your anus with the breath. This is the base *kundalini* energy that you are going to transform, through tantra, to the highest *kundalini* energy that will explode from your crown chakra.

As you draw in the watery *kundalini* energy see it as a dark blood-red fluid, sluggish, cool, deep, all-burning, all-powerful, sleepy mud. Imagine this blood-red fluid being transformed to a lighter red as it reaches the second chakra – the *swadhishthana* – located at the genitals. Then imagine the water travelling to the third chakra at the navel – the *manipuraka* – and getting lighter still, an orangey yellow. On to the next chakra located at the heart – *anahata* – and turning into a stronger yellow with tints of green as if life was being stirred into it. Then on to the throat chakra – the *vishuddha* – and turning blue, the blue water of truth and purity. Then up to the brow chakra – the *ajna* – and the water turning bluish-purple, mauve, pale violet. And finally imagine the water reaching the crown chakra and turning completely white – the *sahasrara*. Imagine the water gaining heat and becoming liquid fire – the white hot fire of molten iron. Imagine this fire, this cosmic volcano, erupting out of the top of your head like fire giving birth to the entire universe. Keep rocking as you do this practical assignment as this rocking is the pump that will move this *kundalini* energy up your entire body.

The way energy moves

For men and women the energy moves differently. The man will feel this energy slowly working its way up his spine, while for you the energy will rise slowly up through the belly first and then the breasts. The man's energy, being hotter and more volatile, may well rise faster but he should not rush it. Your energy, being cooler and slower to arouse, will take longer. If during any exercise either of you becomes aroused to the point of orgasm then that's all right. Because we are orgasm oriented in the West it may take a while to learn to focus on the energy rather than the sexual experience. Whatever way you do it, it should be an enjoyable experience.

The approach of delight

The whole basis of raising the *kundalini* energy is to share and experience the 'godhead' – if this isn't done in a spirit of delight and enjoyment it will not be successful. There are some who have spent a whole lifetime practising tantric sex and getting nowhere because they do the whole thing as a ritual and miss the point completely.

You have to enter into tantric sex with an approach of delight – what happens is happening and it's all right. Sometimes there will be a union of soul with soul and sometimes not – but the journey should be enjoyed without thought of the destination, or the experience that is presented along the way will be lost.

If, during any practical assignment, you become excited, orgasmic – enjoy it. There should be no spiritual ego to taunt your partner with – 'Oh, I attained enlightenment and all you achieved was orgasm.'

Reunion with God

Use the experience as it comes and try to use the energy in a beneficial way. The principle aim or objective of raising the *kundalini* energy is to reunite or connect with the energy of the universe through the unique and wonderful experience of sex – tantra is a reunion with God.

Appreciating

During any exercise the energy may become very sleepy – go with it and use the time given as a meditation. Focus on the brow chakra (see page 71) and allow yourself to appreciate what you can see, feel and hear. There is a reason, according to the tantric Buddhists, why the energy can take any one of many different forms. It may be orgasmic, meditative or spiritually enlightening – it may even be all three – but the energy generated is being transformed into exactly what you need at any given moment. It may not be what you expect – or even what you particularly want – but it will be what you need. The tantric Buddhists recommend that you go with it – if you don't fight the Universe it will provide you with everything you need.

Practical assignment: Being in touch with your body

Doing this exercise will put you in touch with how you feel about your sexual body. You can do this alone or for the benefit of your partner. Our genitals are our sexual parts and we often consider them as somehow separate from the rest of our body. We find pet names for them or vulgar ones or even funny ones – what do you call your vagina? What do you call your breasts? Your clitoris?

How do you feel about your sexual parts? Do you view them as healthy and wholesome or somehow vulgar and dirty? If you truly want to explore tantric sex you have to have a clean and wholesome view of your sexual parts. If you are to be open and share in an honest way your sexuality with your partner you have to love your sexual parts as much as you expect them to. If you don't, then how can you truly relax and be sexually enlightened? According to the tantric Buddhists one of the reasons we sometimes fail to achieve a truly deep spiritual/sexual experience is because we are somehow hanging onto our fears and repression. During this exercise you can explore your feelings about your sexuality and your body as a sexual instrument.

With your right hand cover your vagina as if you are hiding it. Your left hand should be placed on your belly and begin to slowly circle your stomach in a clockwise direction. As you rub you should begin to feel heat here. You don't have to run quickly but do rub firmly. As you rub close your eyes and shift your focus to your vagina. Slowly move your hand away as if your hand was a flower unfolding in the morning sun. You are slowly revealing your womanhood, your sex, your root chakra. How does this feel? Are you proud of what you are revealing or should it be kept hidden?

You should aim to rub your belly 100 times but don't worry too much about counting as your focus should be on your sexual parts. With your right hand slowly open the vaginal entrance, peeling back your labia to reveal the secret entrance. How does this feel? If you are doing this with, and for, the benefit of your partner, what thoughts are now going through your head?

Releasing energy for women

In Chapter 05 we looked at this point at storing energy for men. In women there is no need for this. Men's energy is hot and volatile, easily spent and needing constant replenishment. Women's energy, however, is sluggish, deep, dark, con-centrated, huge and complex. Whereas men's energy needs to be invigorated and recharged – stored in their belly and built up – your energy needs to be released, made hotter and more fluid, stirred up, made more volatile, energized and generally encouraged to flow more easily. The Taoists call female energy *yin* which means many things, including nurturing. The whole aim of sex in Taoist tantric practices is to get the hot male energy to penetrate the female energy and fire a bolt of fire into it to heat it up. Taoists equate the female energy with a vast cauldron of dark liquid. The male energy is the fire which heats this cauldron up. Male energy needs to be moved up from the sexual organs to the belly where it can be heated and stored. Female energy needs to be moved down from the belly – where it is hotter and more fluid – to your sexual organs where it can be used to dilate the *yin* energy and enable you to become quicker and more sexual. The next practical assignment is to get you to move this energy downwards and to make it more fluid and heat it up. You have already begun this process in the previous exercise by rubbing your belly in a clockwise direction.

Practical assignment: Releasing energy for women

Sit naked and cross-legged on the floor. Again make sure you are comfortable, warm and safe – no interruptions. Place your left hand on your belly and rub 100 times clockwise. Do this slowly but firmly. Feel the heat generated there. Close your eyes and imagine this energy, this heat, slowly trickling down towards your vagina. Imagine it as light energy, silver, hot, volatile. See it dripping into the vast pool of dark *yin* energy that is your female sexuality. As each drop falls into the cauldron of *yin*, imagine it spreading through the dark nurturing energy making it all hot and lighter, thinner and more ready to flow, to erupt upwards through the seven chakras. You can do this practical assignment before having sex and you will easily be able to match your partner's speed to orgasm, their readiness to come.

Once you have allowed this belly energy to flow downwards and have imagined your *yin* cauldron as heated up and made more volatile and thinner you can allow this heat to spread upwards again throughout your entire body. See your whole body as a vast vagina waiting to accept the male seed. Keep breathing. Keep focused and use your PC muscle to pump this energy upwards. It will travel up your belly, between your breasts to the brow chakra and thence to the crown chakra where it can be reunited with the male energy. Imagine the universe as a male shower of semen raining down on your head and that your hot female energy is waiting to accept it, to absorb it, to neutralize it – this is the nurturing aspect, you are easing the pain of all that heat a man feels.

Summary

In this chapter we have looked at ways of improving our sexual performance and the spiritual side of our sexuality. We have looked at and explored in our practical assignments the four stages of sexual excitement, arousal and orgasm.

We have learnt about the PC (pubococcygeus) muscle and how developing it can enhance our oragasms. We learnt when and how to do practical assignments to improve our PC muscle and combined such practice with PC muscle breathing. This helps us to both enhance our sexual experience at the point of orgasm as well as enhancing the spiritual side of sex.

We looked at the seven chakras – energy centres – and learnt how to 'open' them and explore the energy of each one. We also learnt how, according to tantric principles, energy moves in our body and how the flow of energy can be enhanced and strengthened.

07

meditation for men and women

In this chapter you will learn:
- different meditations
- Zen meditations
- raja yoga meditations.

The languishing eye
Connects soul with soul
And the tender kiss
Takes the message from member to vulva.
                              Perfumed Garden

Practical assignment: Meditation

Try each of the following meditations until you find one that you like: one that works and that allows you to experience something of what is happening energy-wise internally for you.

Music meditation

- Find somewhere comfortable to sit where you won't be disturbed. Close your eyes and listen to your favourite piece of music – classical music works best.
- As the music plays – Verdi is very good for this – allow your thoughts to wash over you. Don't try to control them or channel them. Just simply listen and see where your thoughts lead you.
- Let the music wash over you. You may find this easier with stereo headphones. When the music finishes just enjoy the silence for a while and feel the energy moving within you.

Walking meditation

- Go for a walk in the countryside or park on your own. This is a walk with no purpose apart from relaxing. You aren't walking your dog or going anywhere in particular. You aren't exercising or getting fit. You are going to go for a walk purely and simply to relax.
- Don't look around you particularly, but try to focus ahead so you can see where you are going but you are not looking at anything in particular.
- Let thoughts come to you, but always try to remember that you are walking to meditate.
- Feel the motion of your body through the countryside and be aware of the feel of the air on your face, the smells, the sense of being outdoors.
- Allow your breathing to be very relaxed, using your diaphragm rather than upper chest. Occasionally, take a deep breath to free up any tension you may have.

- Allow about 20 minutes several times a week to walk purely for pleasure and relaxation with no other purpose – the dog can wait until later.
- As you walk, feel the energy in you, around you, and how connected to the rest of the cosmos you are.

Breathing meditation

- Find somewhere to sit comfortably where you won't be disturbed.
- Let your hands fall naturally into your lap and close your eyes.
- Allow all the tension in your neck and shoulders to drop away. You might like to shrug your shoulders up to your ears and then let them drop.
- Concentrate on your breathing. Breathe in through your nose and out through your mouth. With each in-breath mentally say the word 'sexual'; with each out-breath mentally say the word 'energy'.
- Breathe for about ten minutes like this and then slowly return to normal life and see how sexy you feel. You can do this one on the train, in the office, waiting for a bus, while watching television or even in the bath. If anyone interrupts you and you don't want to say you were meditating, you can just say you were thinking deeply or daydreaming.

Heartbeat meditation

- Find somewhere comfortable to sit where you won't be disturbed.
- Place your left hand on your upper chest.
- Bring your right hand round so that you can feel the pulse in your left wrist with your right index and forefinger.
- Close your eyes and feel your pulse.
- Count the pulse at the same time as you allow your breathing to drop to your abdomen and become relaxed.
- Once you have got the count of the pulse, start to count your breathing as well.
- Unless you cheat, it is almost impossible to count both breaths and pulse at the same time but it wonderfully absorbs your mind for a while allowing deep relaxation to take place.
- If you stop thinking, you start feeling.

Forehead meditation

- Find somewhere to sit comfortably where you won't be disturbed.
- Close your eyes and look at the inside of your forehead.
- Try to imagine a small ball of blue light there.
- Concentrate on this area for about five or ten minutes. If you see any blue light then you are witnessing a physical manifestation of your own inner energy – you are seeing God.

Deep-breathing meditation

- Find somewhere to sit comfortably where you won't be disturbed.
- Place your hands on your abdomen so that your fingertips are just touching.
- Concentrate on abdominal breathing.
- With each in-breath your stomach should expand and your fingertips part. With each out-breath your stomach should contract and your fingertips come back together again.
- Concentrate on the movement of your fingers for five or ten minutes.
- Feel how the energy moves in your body.

Tasting meditation

- You can do this one anywhere and with your eyes open or closed, although it works best with them closed.
- Fold your tongue back until it touches the roof of your mouth. With the tip of your tongue explore the sensation of the roof of your mouth. What can you taste? What does it feel like? Try it with your teeth together. Swallow if you need to.
- After you have explored the sensations for a while allow your tongue to become still, just resting lightly on the roof of your mouth. Concentrate on this for five minutes or so and then stop.
- When you are doing your PC breathing, keep your tongue lightly resting on the roof of your mouth as it makes an energy connection – a sort of switch – allowing energy to reach up through your brow chakra to your crown chakra. Imagine the energy as if moving along an electric cable with a switch in it. The tongue is this switch and you need to 'earth' it by pressing it to the roof of your mouth.

Prone meditation

- Find somewhere to lie down quietly where you won't be disturbed.
- Lie flat on your back with your arms by your side.
- Imagine that you are an inert body – completely relaxed and without movement.
- Allow your breathing to become very still and slow from your abdomen.
- Close your eyes and imagine you are floating.
- Let your body become as light as a feather.
- Stay like this for ten minutes and then return to normal.

Listening meditation

- Find somewhere quiet where you won't be disturbed.
- Sit down in a comfortable chair with your feet flat on the floor.
- Place a cushion in your lap and rest your elbows on it.
- Reach up and gently place a thumb in each ear and allow the other fingers to rest lightly on the top of your head.
- Listen to the sounds coming from inside your body – your breathing, your heartbeat and the blood pumping through your body.
- Stay like this for as long as you want to or until your arms become uncomfortable. You may have to lean slightly forwards to get really comfortable. You can also try this one propped up in bed last thing at night just before going to sleep.
- Listen not only to your body sounds but to anything else you may hear – this may well be the sounds of the energy moving within your body.

Once you have done a few of these very simple meditations you are ready to move on to deeper meditation so that you can experience something of that inner energy. One of the simplest methods is to orgasm. During orgasm you lose all sense of yourself and merge – albeit it very briefly – with the essence of the godhead within you. Tantric practices attempt to prolong this brief spasm so you can enjoy and experience it for longer, deeper and more frequently, but there are other methods of appreciating this energy.

Practical assignment: Zen meditation

Find a room that has a white wall where you won't be disturbed. No other colour seems to work as well. Sit cross-legged facing this wall. Your knees should be about one inch away from the wall. Allow yourself to become as relaxed as possible. If you need to prop yourself up on cushions that's fine, just so long as you don't make yourself so comfortable that you fall asleep.

Stare directly ahead at the wall. The whole object of Zen is to sit back and wait to see what happens. The white wall becomes a screen on which your mind can project anything it wants. Allow your thoughts to rise and drift away naturally. The beauty of this is that you don't have to do anything. Just sit. Just watch. Just wait.

Once you have practised this meditation for a few weeks – and you only have to devote around half an hour a day to it – you will get used to sitting still, doing nothing, being quiet, stilling your mind and generally entering a more tranquil place where the inner energy – which is very subtle – can be appreciated. Now you are ready to go even deeper.

Practical assignment: Raja yoga meditation

For this one you'll need a very quiet, comfortable place where there is absolutely no likelihood of being disturbed. If you have a lock on your bedroom door then this is a good place. Take the phone off the hook and make sure there is nothing pressing for you to do – you need to be relaxed and not worrying about getting this done so you can go to work or pick the kids up from school.

Sit cross-legged in the middle of the bed and place a large pillow across your knees. You need to do several things at once so read the following before starting the meditation:

- Put the tip of your tongue on the back of the roof of your mouth to 'close the circuit'.
- Carry out your PC breathing.
- Put your elbows on the pillow and close off your ears with your hands; cup them over your ears quite tightly to shut out all sound.
- Close your eyes.
- Focus your eyes and attention on the centre of your forehead – the third eye.

- Lower your head and sink down into the pillow so you are comfortable and relaxed.

You are now effectively shut down and completely turned inwards. Now there is a space, an opportunity, for the inner energy to 'speak' to you. They say that if prayer is talking to God then meditation is listening to the answer. This is the listening. Watch what happens in the space inside your own head where the brow chakra is located – between the eyes and slightly above. Feel the breath entering and leaving your body. Feel the pull of the energy through your PC muscle being sent upwards. Listen to what is happening inside your own body. Initially you may only hear the rush of blood and your heartbeat, but there is a space here for the energy to make its own song.

Practise this for about half an hour twice a day if you can. Time is always in short supply, but this meditation will put you in touch with the energy deeper and more lastingly than any other.

Summary

By combining the meditation practical assignments and the individual sex practical assignments you should both be now ready to move onto the tantric sex practical assignments for couples. The next chapter is the one for both of you to read and work through together. Some things you'll enjoy, others you may not. Some things will work for you, still others may not. Whatever you do, do it with a spirit of enjoyment. Go with the flow and have a laugh, smile, be in love, be loving, be gentle with each other and have fun. The principle of tantric sex is spiritual transformation through sex and through pleasure. If you ain't enjoying it – *don't do it!*

08

practical assignments for couples

In this chapter you will learn:
- some tantric yoga relaxations
- about different types of orgasm
- about tantric kissing.

Contemporary approaches to sexuality are very restricted. Practitioners of Tantra maintain that by transforming the context of sex, we can transform the experience. Tantric exercises focus on vitality, sensuality and relationship rather than sexuality in the limited way we usually understand it.

Cassandra Lorius, *Tantric Sex*

You should, by now, have both been practising tantric techniques individually. Now you can come together to explore your sexuality and spirituality. Before you do, you need to explore your sexual environment. Where and when do you make love? What signals do you give to each other prior to making love? Who is responsible for clearing the bedroom prior to making love? Who chooses the music? Do you have music? And what about candlelight? These things are all worthy of consideration and constitute your sexual environment. Some of them are things we never think about. That isn't a tantric approach. The tantric approach is to be awake, be aware of every detail. If we make love in an unconscious manner, which is the norm for most people, our pleasure levels will remain low and bland. If we concentrate on all the important details and stay focused, our pleasure levels can soar.

The boudoir

Let's start with the basic room. It is assumed you share a bedroom, although there is no reason written in stone as to why you should. You may be a couple, but you are still both independent, adult, grown-up people who are entitled to a measure of esteem and respect from each other. Sharing a bedroom may work for you, but if it doesn't you should seriously consider having separate rooms. We are all individuals and have our own tastes and styles. It can repress our sexuality if we are living in someone else's space and not feeling ourselves.

Bedrooms are for sleeping in. Boudoirs are for making love in. Is your room a bedroom or a boudoir? They are different. You can use the same room for both purposes – sleeping and making love – but you need to change the room for each occasion. Making love is a sacred event and it simply isn't good enough – well, at least not for modern tantric purposes – to make love on a bed with unclean, rumpled sheets or with clothing lying around on the floor, dirty cups by the bed, old magazines and books piled up, suitcases stored on top of the wardrobe – that sort of thing.

Your boudoir needs to be:

* clean and fresh
* newly decorated
* clear of all clutter.

The bed should have:

* fresh clean linen
* been freshly made
* no clutter around it.

Now you have the basics of a boudoir. You have a bed freshly made with clean linen – preferably white (no other colour seems to work as well and some colours can give skin tones weird coloration that isn't harmonious to good sex) – and a newly decorated room – again preferably white but you can be wilder here and go for reds, but no floral wallpapers, please – so what's next?

Atmosphere is a very important part of tantric sex. You are going to enter a world of spirituality and want to enhance the feeling of being in the presence of an experience of that inner energy. You don't want distraction. You don't want to be reminded of the outside world. Tidy up all clutter and light candles. Play pleasant music – classical is probably best. Incense works well as it perfumes the air and helps create an atmosphere of something special going on.

If you have a log or coal fire, brilliant – or even a wood-burning stove. This too helps set the scene and helps remind you that something very primordial and natural is happening.

Now you should both be about ready for your first practical assignment together.

Practical assignment: Mutual masturbation

This practical assignment is to get you both used to enjoying each other's orgasm without any pressure. Mutual masturbation can create a richer sexual life because it gives both of you the opportunity to experiment with what brings the most pleasure, without the pressure of performing or having to have full penetrative sex. Each of you can 'lie back' and enjoy yourselves and your orgasm, and the spiritual experience, without having to do too much yourself – perfect pleasure.

You can set the scene with soft lights, romantic music and if you both are happy to include it, an erotic video. If you like, use lubrication such as baby oil on the penis or the vulva. There are a range of positions for mutual masturbastion. The only practical requirement is for both of your genitals to be within easy reach. You could both lie side by side, with the woman's upper body resting on the man's. You can then both easily reach the other's genital area and the man can kiss the woman's face and neck and stroke her hair.

At the same time he can feel her breasts with his hands. Her hand is free to guide his towards doing what she likes best and the other can reach toward his body and stimulate his penis. Mutual masturbation is an alternative to penetrative sex and can add interest to a couple's sex life. For example, when the man cannot get an erection or a woman is pregnant, has just had a baby or some recent surgery or either of the couple is tired and penetrative sex may not be an option. Many people enjoy non-penetrative sex as an exciting sexual option. Part of the tantra of mutual masturbation is deciding on who comes first – and then what happens? Sometimes, one partner might like to come first and then go to sleep without 'repaying the favour'. This is fine as long as no one is left feeling left out or frustrated. Perhaps this could take place over two evenings so each partner gets a turn. But don't make it race – although to see who can come first might be an interesting variation occasionally.

Previously you have explored your chakras by doing the chakra meditation. Now you can come together and combine these individual meditations and do them together.

Practical assignment: Chakra meditation for couples

For the man

You should lie down somewhere warm and comfortable. Imagine the site of each chakra as a small, tightly-furled flower or small leather bag. As you breathe out make the mantra sound for each chakra as you visualize it in turn, starting with the base chakra and finishing with the brow chakra. Imagine each chakra as a flower opening as you breathe out – or the small leather bag having draw strings which are being slowly loosened.

Work your way up the body, imagining each chakra opening as you make the mantra sound as you exhale. You need to do this exercise with your eyes closed so you can visualize each chakra in turn. This exercise can be done before you make love with your partner so that you are fully open and ready to feel energy moving within your body.

For the woman

You should lie down somewhere warm and comfortable. Imagine each chakra as a flower turned upside down. As you breathe out make the sound of the chakra mantra and imagine each chakra in turn, starting with the base chakra and finishing with the crown chakra, as the flower slowly turning until it is upright. As it does so, imagine it becoming cooler and stiller as if filled with cold refreshing energy.

You should do this exercise before making love with your partner so that your chakras are open and you are ready to feel the energy moving within your body.

You can also do this exercise as a method of cleansing or purifying your energy. As you visualize your energy reaching the crown chakra, imagine it pouring out of the top of your head and being replaced with fresh new energy from your base chakra. Imagine all the collected energy of all your past lovers being replaced so that you can begin again with a fresh supply.

Now you need to begin to explore how the energy in each of you moves. This next practical assignment will relax you and allow you to feel the energy moving in your partner. Take your time and enjoy the sensations and feelings.

Practical assignment: Tantric yoga relaxation position (*muladhara sadhana*)

Both you and your lover lie down side by side on your backs but facing opposite ways – your feet to their head and their feet to your head. The man should lie with the woman along his right side so he can place his hand lightly across her vulva. The woman can then use her right hand to hold his penis lightly.

This is an exercise to feel the energy rising from the base chakra up through the pelvic chakra and beyond. Try to feel the warmth your partner's hand generates in and through your genitals. As the warmth spreads, focus on it and feel it spreading upwards as energy.

The man will feel this energy slowly working its way up his spine, while for the woman the energy will rise slowly up through the belly first and then the breasts. The man's energy, being hotter and more volatile, may well rise faster but he should not rush it. The woman's energy, being cooler and slower to arouse, will take longer. If during this exercise either becomes aroused to the point of orgasm then that's all right.

Yab yum

There is a sexual position which is known in tantra as *yab yum* (sometimes also known as *yab yom*). This is probably the most widely used and effective sexual position for feeling the inner energy moving. Take your time to enjoy using this position without having to worry about orgasms or anything else. In this position you will never be closer to your partner.

Practical assignment: Yab yum

The man should sit on the floor and the woman should straddle him. He should insert his erect penis into her vulva but neither should move. If the woman grasps the man around his back and he holds her around her shoulders you should both be able to relax and feel comfortable. You should look into each other's eyes. The tantric texts suggest that you should both keep your tongue on the roof of your mouth as this helps the energy complete its circuit around your body.

You should both feel the warmth coming from each other's pelvic chakra and concentrate on feeling the energy rising up.

The woman should feel the energy as a cool flow rising slowly up the front of her body. The man should feel the energy as a hot flow rising up his spine. This position is more about meditation than sex although you may both orgasm in this position without moving. It gives you both a chance to relax and feel or visualize the energy moving without any expectations. It's also very good for lovers who have problems with the man experiencing premature ejaculation. As there is no movement, no thrusting excitement, he should be able to keep his penis in position for quite a while before experiencing ejaculation. Again there are no expectations. If you don't feel any energy moving you can visualize it instead. If only one of you feels the energy then that's also fine.

Sometimes this position is very good prior to making love as a means of establishing a contact, a sort of spiritual reaffirmation of your love for each other. How long you spend in this position is entirely up to you. It's something you need to find out by experimentation. For some couples a few minutes seem to be enough, while other couples will enjoy this position so much that they are content to spend a considerable amount of time doing it.

If you do tire you can always lean back for a while and rest. You may even like to experiment by eating or drinking while doing this.

You can talk to each other, tell each other stories. This position is about relaxing with each other, feeling the energy and trust. You don't have to do anything, go anywhere. Just be together in the most intimate way without wanting the other to be anything or anyone else – just themselves.

You can always try experimenting if you find this position uncomfortable. The man can sit in a chair, one without arms like a wooden kitchen chair, and the woman can sit astride him. He can then support her with his hands on her hips and she can rest her arms on his shoulders or even grip the back of the chair.

It may seem a strange notion to Westerners that we can physically exchange energy during sex. However, there are some practical exercises you can do which may convince you of the reality of such an experience as well as allowing you to experiment freely with your own energy and that of your partner.

The Hindu tantric practitioners write about the energy as the *kundalini* – the coiled serpent – while the Chinese Taoists call it *ch'i*.

If you are practising your practical assignments you may well now have an understanding of this energy. Previously we explained how keeping your tongue touching the roof of your mouth formed a sort of switch for the energy to move to the brow chakra. This is to allow the energy to complete its circuit around the body freely. By using our tongue like this we can feel the energy as it flows. The Chinese believe the tongue to be an internal organ – the only one we can see and experience externally. It is a very sensitive instrument and can channel and control the energy in a very delicate way. During our lovemaking we instinctively lick and suck parts of our lover's body. As well as producing exquisite pleasure in them it is also an instinctive attempt to experience that energy – and it can be done so much more effectively if we do it consciously.

One of the ways we can truly experience that energy consciously is when we are kissing. The art of kissing is a skill that takes time to learn and lots of practice if we are to experience it fully. It's an art not often practised in the West. In China, couples won't kiss in public as they regard it as something so intimate, so sexual, that to them it would be like making love in public.

Practical assignment: Tantric kissing

Agree with your partner to spend as much time practising tantric kissing as you can. You can use your lips and tongue to explore your partner's mouth. You can suck their tongue, lick the inside of their lips, nip with your teeth, even exchange saliva – known as the *Juice of Jade* in China. You can use your tongue to explore their entire face – licking their eyelids, ears and the underside of the chin are particularly erotic. If you and your partner suck each other's tongue in turn you may find it quite easy to orgasm spontaneously.

Another aspect of tantric kissing is to use your fingers as well. As you lick and suck on your partner's mouth you can insert your fingers into their mouth and they can suck on your fingers as well. Obviously in all of these practical assignments some degree of personal hygiene is important – cleaning your teeth beforehand and avoiding strong tasting or smelling foods.

You can use your tongue to explore your partner's hands. The skin between the fingers is especially sensitive. Most men report that having their thumbs sucked is very erotic both because of its resemblance to oral sex but also because of the sensitivity of the thumb.

Practical assignment: Skin exploration

You can use your tongue to explore the entire skin area of your partner's body. To completely lick every part of another's body takes longer than you might think – but it's worth it. You get to know them pretty intimately as well as finding out exactly what turns them on, which bits they like licked the best. It's quite common to expect the erogenous zones to be sensitive but you may be surprised to find that the crook of the elbow produces such a strong reaction, or the armpit, the bottom of the feet or the back of the knees.

Nipples are very sensitive as are navels, throats, foreheads and genitals – these are the areas of the chakras. It's not just that these areas are sensitive because they're sexy – they are also major energy centres.

While you are doing this practical assignment you should be concentrating both on giving your partner pleasure and also on feeling what their energy is doing – as well as feeling what energy you are experiencing. If you take your time you may well begin to feel tiny electric currents in your tongue as you reach the right spot on their body where they are generating energy as well.

You could also try visualizing energy as tiny sparks jumping from the tip of your tongue. If you do this you may find your partner reacts differently – as if there really are sparks flying.

Practical assignment: Tongue energy

After a time spent erotically kissing and exploring all the skin of your partner's body, you may like to bring them to orgasm using your tongue and lips only – no hands or other parts at all. Again, concentrate on the energy being generated. As you lick and suck you can try visualizing that energy – see it as tiny sparks jumping from the end of your tongue. If you keep your eyes closed try to concentrate on the area between your eyebrows and in the centre of your forehead – the *third eye*. Watch what happens there as you reach orgasm yourself. Instead of seeing darkness you may be surprised by how much light is generated by the energy of the *kundalini* reaching the top of your head. This is energy you can see as well as feel.

When you are bringing your partner to orgasm, feel what happens to the tip of your tongue – can you feel the energy? When you are reaching your own orgasm, keep your tongue on the roof of your mouth and feel what happens.

Practical assignment: Tantric kissing for experienced lovers

Bring your partner to orgasm using your hands. As they reach orgasm they should stick their tongue out and you can suck it quite hard and practise the tantric kissing techniques. They should bring you to orgasm and you can try the same thing – feel what happens to your tongue when it is sucked hard as you reach orgasm.

After orgasm you should always practise erotic kissing together – it promotes intimacy as well as being an extremely sensitive way of keeping the energy flowing. If you don't subside too far after orgasm it's easier to continue.

Practical assignment: Drinking in the soul

Let your partner bring themselves to orgasm while you practise erotic kissing with them. Use your fingers to explore their mouth as well as your lips and tongue. As they reach orgasm hold their face in your hands and get them to keep their eyes open. Look deeply into their eyes and watch what happens there as they orgasm. Then it's your turn. Keep your eyes open as you reach orgasm and look into your partner's eyes.

This exercise requires a considerable degree of intimacy, love and trust. This is one of those exercises you couldn't do with a casual sexual partner as you are allowing your partner access to the most intimate, inner part of you. It certainly requires trust to be able to do, but if you try it you may well find it an incredible experience – one that you will want to repeat often. It raises sex from being a merely physical pleasure to being one of such intensity and spirituality that you wonder why you haven't been doing it for years.

Practical assignment: Perineum orgasm

We are used to bringing our partners to orgasm by concentrating our energies on their pelvic chakra – but what about trying the other chakras? The nipples are in the region of the heart chakra. Try bringing your partner to orgasm by sucking, licking, feeling, pinching, tweaking, whatever, their nipples – and they can try doing the same to you.

Try bringing them to orgasm by concentrating your loving on their throat chakra, or brow chakra, or navel chakra. And don't forget the base chakra. This you can locate midway between the genitals and the anus. It's called the *perineum* and it is extremely sensitive. You can try bringing your partner to orgasm by licking this area or massaging it with your fingers. A woman can get her partner to insert his fingers into her anus and vagina and then the perineum can be gripped and massaged internally. For the man the area underneath the testicles can be massaged as well as a finger being inserted into the rectum. Obviously these techniques require hygiene – if you insert a finger into your partner's anus you should wash your hands before using your fingers anywhere else. And if your partner has any reservations about such techniques then those reservations should be respected – as should yours.

Practical assignment: Following *kundalini* energy

Using your tongue follow the path the *kundalini* energy would follow in your partner's body. For the man this is up the spine. The woman can start with her tongue on her partner's perineum and trace the passage of the energy up his buttocks and spine to the top of his head. She can continue down his brow, throat, chest and back to the perineum. The man can masturbate while the woman is doing this and they can feel the energy rising in different ways. The man can visualize the energy as it goes up through the chakras.

For the woman, the energy rises the opposite way so the man should trace the energy flow up the front of her body. He should start with his tongue on his partner's perineum and trace the path from her vulva, up across her belly, between her breasts, up her throat to her brow and then stop at the crown of her head. If she masturbates while he does this you should aim to time it so that orgasm happens as the man's tongue reaches the crown of the head. As the orgasm subsides the man should run his tongue down her spine and back to the perineum.

Practical assignment: Exploring temperature

You can try experimenting with different temperatures on your tongue. Keep some ice cubes handy as well as a hot drink, such as coffee. You can dip your tongue into these alternately and see what effect it has on your partner. Try practising oral sex using ice cubes or coffee held in the mouth so your partner gets the full effect of the heightened temperature. As they reach orgasm you can try suddenly switching the temperature and see what happens. Try running ice cubes over their nipples or genitals – whatever you fancy. You can only learn about the energy by experimenting. And you can only experiment by having fun.

Further practical assignments for men

In Chapter 05 we looked at such techniques as the squeeze and the lock. Now there is an opportunity for the man to try some of these ejaculation delaying techniques with his partner.

We also looked earlier at the way the Taoists regard *yin* and *yang* energy, the male and female principles. Yang, the male principle, is fire, while yin, the female principle, is water. Fire is quick and spontaneous and can be easily extinguished by water. Water is much slower to heat up but, once hot, takes much longer to cool down. Together they can be a powerful force. If you poured water over a fire it would just go out – but if you were to use the fire to heat the water in a pot then it would boil and could be used for cooking or washing or whatever other purpose you desired. This analogy of the cooking pot is a Taoist one. The woman is often described as the *yin cauldron* and the man as the *yang furnace*.

The peak of ching

The yin energy is said to reside in a woman's belly – the cauldron – while a man's fire resides in his testicles – the furnace. Once that fire has briefly flared up in ejaculation he is extinguished until he has had time to recover. The Taoists believed that the male orgasm, known as the *Peak of Ching* (*ching* being translated as spirit) could be separate from his ejaculation. The yang spirit, *ching*, is said to be stored in the kidneys by Chinese medical practitioners. This spirit can be both physical – sperm – and ethereal – *ch'i* energy. Men who ejaculate at orgasm are losing both the physical and the spiritual type of *ching*. The Taoists recommended that the man tries to hold onto the physical part of *ching* as much as possible. Losing *ching* causes ill health, retaining *ching* leads to longevity and good health.

Retaining the seed

Orgasm without ejaculation is known as *retaining the seed*. It doesn't mean you can't orgasm. It only means that there is a distinct difference between orgasm and ejaculation. Once that concept is accepted, the following exercises may become easier. Even if you don't manage the retaining of seed your efforts will not have been wasted – all the following exercises will enable you to have sex for much longer without orgasm, learn more about being a better and more considerate lover, and help you get and keep an erection more easily. None of these things will go unappreciated by your partner.

Learning experience

Whereas some of these exercises can be done alone, it will be assumed that you and your partner are practising tantric sex together and that neither one of you is more or less experienced than the other. If the true delights of tantric sex are to be learnt, enjoyed and used then all it takes is practice. In the West we tend to have sex when our passions are aroused, when the opportunity presents itself or even out of habit. However, we are now studying Eastern practices and that means sex is a learning experience. A time and place has to be set aside for practise.

Ritual sex

Mood and passion don't really play a part in this learning process. It may sound a little cold and clinical to 'book' a time for sex and to discuss beforehand which exercises you are going to do – but this is only for a while. Once you have learnt each other's rhythms, methods and means you can return to mood and passion with a new- found experience and wisdom that will more than compensate for the time spent 'in the classroom'. These 'training sessions' should also be fun. Make sure you are warm enough and that your surroundings are harmonious and conducive to good lovemaking.

Practical assignment: The lock

The couple should have sex with passion and vigour and the man should ejaculate – then they are ready to begin. They should have sex again. This time the man, especially if he is young and sexually inexperienced, will be much less likely to orgasm quite so quickly the second time – or even third or fourth if he is full of *ching*. The man should be 'on top'. He should practise the *Thrusts of the Heron*. This is where he pushes his *Jade Hammer*, penis, into the woman's *Jade Gate*, vulva, three times deeply and then once quite shallowly. This will enable him to almost withdraw his Jade Hammer on the fourth or shallow stroke if he feels himself about to orgasm. As he almost withdraws, he should arch his back and 'suck' in his lower abdomen. This is known as the 'locking' position and it should help him avoid orgasm. Obviously he must be aware of how close he is and not leave it too late. The Thrusts of the Heron can go on for as long as he likes unless he feels the imminence of orgasm when he should carry out the locking position. When the feeling of near orgasm has subsided he can continue with the heron thrusts.

Once you are experienced with the heron thrusts you might like to move on to the *Thrusts of the Dragon*. This is where the man thrusts deeply nine times and then once quite shallowly. Again he should carry out the locking position if he feels an orgasm coming on.

Once mastered, the Thrusts of the Dragon can be reversed for the *Thrusts of the Phoenix*. This is where the man thrusts very shallowly for nine strokes and then once very deeply. Women who have never been able to have a vaginal orgasm report that the phoenix thrusts are often the very movements that enable them to have one for the first time.

What to think about

Modern sex therapists often suggest that the man should not think about sex if he wants to retain ejaculation control, but should instead count or recite something or even, believe it or not, work out his monthly bills. However, we are learning tantric sex techniques and no such advice would ever be given here. The man, if he suffers from premature ejaculation, would be much better off learning the locking method which would both help him and certainly go a long way towards giving his partner pleasure and satisfaction. You could always concentrate on the texture of your partner's hair or the quality of her skin, but be present, be there in the act as much as possible. Counting and bill paying are nothing to do with sex.

Practical assignment: The squeeze technique

The couple should have sex in the same way as described in the previous practical assignment. The same techniques of the heron, dragon and phoenix thrusts can be used. When the man feels he is reaching orgasm, instead of withdrawing his Jade Hammer he should use his index and forefinger to press quite hard on the perineum – the small area situated between the scrotum and the anus – the site of the base chakra. Obviously, different men will need different pressure and only you can find out how much you need, but sufficient pressure should be used so that the orgasm subsides. The first few times you try this you may even lose your erection, but this is only because the technique is new. Once you've done it a few times you will be able to maintain your erection quite easily.

The main difference between the locking method and the 'squeeze' method is that the man can quite easily do it himself without disturbing his partner's rhythm. His partner can obviously do it for him if this is preferred.

Once these two methods are learnt, ejaculation control can become an easier concept to deal with. It also makes it much more satisfying for the woman as her partner will be able to keep his thrusting up indefinitely.

The Art of a Thousand Thrusts

The ancient Taoist love texts suggested that a man was quite capable of a thousand thrusts without once feeling the need to orgasm. This may be a bit of Taoist bravado, but any increase must be beneficial – especially for your partner.

Cautions

The tantric texts also suggest that none of these things should be done too quickly. If you have been used to making love every night and always ejaculating, your body is obviously going to be used to making lots of sperm. If you suddenly stop you may experience some tightness or discomfort in the scrotum, so phase it in slowly. Some men also experience a feeling of exhaustion if they don't ejaculate as frequently as normal when they initially start this technique. Try having sex and ejaculating only every other time to begin with.

The Plateau of Delight

Once the lock and squeeze is mastered, the man may well start to experience the *Plateau of Delight*. This wonderful expression is a Taoist way of describing the ejaculateless orgasm. This is where the man has all the sensations of the orgasm without the emission. The Plateau of Delight can be experienced as many times as you like because there is no loss of energy accompanying it. The Plateau of Delight is also just that – a plateau – which implies, quite surprisingly, that you can continue to go higher – experience still more pleasure – without reaching a peak.

Other thrusts

Once all this is mastered, the man might like to incorporate some other thrusts into his loveplay:

- **Bear thrusts** – here the man makes very deep thrusts but holds his Jade Hammer in as far as it will go and for as long as possible.
- **Eagle thrusts** – here the man holds his Jade Hammer for a while, motionless, at the entrance to the Jade Gate then, like an eagle swooping after its prey, he thrusts very quickly.
- **Mouse thrusts** – very quick and very shallow.
- **Ox thrusts** – alternate deep and shallow but very slow and ponderous, like an ox.
- **Snake thrusts** – here the man pushes in quite deeply but very slowly.
- **Sparrow thrusts** – here the man makes very shallow thrusts, teasing around the entrance to the Jade Gate.
- **Wild horse thrusts** – here he bucks and thrusts wildly always going in deeply like a wild horse fording a river.

Do experiment with your own variations on these.

Further practical assignments for women

Because of the way most Western women are brought up, it's difficult to entirely escape feelings of guilt associated with sex. In the West there can often be a barrier, either mental or moral, that women experience when it comes to *enjoying* their sexuality. This barrier has to be removed before women can take their true and rightful place as liberated, fully sexual, empowered and satisfied lovers. The practice of tantric sex is a great help in removing that barrier. If enjoying sex was only about enjoying sex then it would not be so helpful; but when you give it a spiritual purpose then it somehow becomes acceptable – you are not just a lover but also a lover of a God, a *Shakti*, a living representation of the female deity on earth – and that's a powerful responsibility – don't let Her down.

The different types of orgasm

The tantric texts have always recognized that women play an important part in sex and that they are 'special' because they can have several different types of orgasm – we will explore those different types and how to achieve them.

For a lot of women in the West, an intimate knowledge of their own bodies is something to be frowned on – it's just not nice. But how can you be the consort of Shiva if you are shy or coy? By exploring our own bodies we learn how they work. When we know how they work we can use that information to help our lover please us and to please them as well.

Whereas the tantric texts frown on male masturbation they regard it as worthwhile, even to be recommended, for women. The yin energy has to be dissipated at times when your lover is not there. By knowing your orgasm well you can relax and enjoy the spiritual aspect without having to worry about technique or false expectations. Begin by knowing the different types of orgasm and how you respond to them.

The clitoral orgasm

The clitoris is located just in front of and above the vaginal opening. The Taoists call it by various names including the Lotus Bud and the Jade Pearl. When stroked and caressed by you or your lover it will bring you to orgasm. Feel that orgasm – how does it manifest throughout your body? Just as you orgasm, try panting vigorously; does it delay or enhance your orgasm? Can you always achieve a clitoral orgasm? Do you need a special time of day? Is your libido lower in the mornings? Where do you go in your mind when you are masturbating? Can you masturbate freely in front of your lover? There are no right or wrong answers.

The vaginal orgasm

As its name implies it is brought about by internal stimulation but how does it feel to you? Is it different from your clitoral orgasm? Can you achieve the vaginal orgasm? Most research suggests that a lot of women need a much longer period of internal stimulation than their male lovers are capable of for them to experience the vaginal orgasm. This is why it's important for men to learn the techniques previously outlined and to be more considerate of their partner's cooler, slower-to-rouse yin energy.

The G-spot orgasm

Most people think the G-spot is a recent invention or discovery – but it's not. The tantric texts talk about the *Hidden Jade Moon* or the *Heart of the Lotus Bud*. The G-spot is to be found about an inch or two inside the vagina on the top wall; it's a small area with a slightly rougher feel to it. Perhaps a good way to find it is to think of it as the underside of the clitoris – the yin or hidden side of the yang or external clitoris. Some women report no extra sensation here while others recommend it as an area to be stimulated for orgasm. The orgasm induced by G-spot stimulation is different from the other two types. If a woman's lover is considerate and skilful, he may well be able to stimulate the G-spot with the head of his penis. This is why a lot of the techniques you will find in tantric sex involve the man making turning or twisting movements with his penis; it affords extra stimulation above and beyond the normal thrusting that most men seem to think is their only option.

All three

Some women, and again it may depend on the patience and skill of their lover, claim that it is possible to have three orgasms simultaneously; one in each of the three areas. This you may like to try, although it's best not to be 'goal oriented' or you may miss the journey. Once we start setting 'targets' we open ourselves up to disappointment and false expectations. However, as an exercise it's useful to know what sort of ultimate is possible; this lets us know what we are capable of. If the male lover is skilful he may be able to use his penis to stimulate the vaginal orgasm and, at the same time, using his thumb and index finger stimulate both the clitoris and G-spot. Some women also report an anal orgasm if their sphincter muscles are stimulated gently.

Nectar of the Moon

The Taoist texts also suggest that a woman is capable of a sort of ejaculation. This seems to be a very moist flow from the urethra (the tube through which women urinate) at the point of orgasm. For some women it is true that they produce copious fluid at that moment while others don't. The Taoists called this the *Nectar of the Moon* and regarded it as most beneficial for men to taste as it was the most highly charged *yin* essence that they could absorb. The Taoists called saliva the *Jade Spring* and also recommended that men could taste it and absorb the *yin* essence from it.

Some women find it quite hard to orgasm during intercourse and need stimulating by hand or orally. This should be incorporated into your lovemaking so that your lover doesn't have to feel he's 'letting you down' or not 'good enough'. Earlier we talked about tantric sex being about communication – and it is. If you don't tell your partner what you want and need he will not be able to read your mind. There are some tantric lovers who seem to know instinctively what a woman requires, but they are usually very experienced in Eastern love techniques and have worked with the energy of sex for years. You and your partner may well be just starting out. If you are new to this form of sex then it's only fair to give your partner some encouragement and help. You will have to go slowly and explain clearly what you need and want and then he will get more skilled and that will benefit both of you. You have to remember that men's Western sexual education was probably as non-existent as your own. Most men are hot impulsive lovers who have to work hard to become considerate patient partners; that's not because they are ill-mannered or rude or selfish – it's merely that they don't know any different; they've never been shown or taught that there is an alternative. Once shown they will never go back to their old way of loving. But you have to tell them what is needed.

Oral loving

When a man loves your vulva with his lips, mouth and tongue he is worshipping the female deity – you are the *Shakti* and you are feeding his energy. Good oral sex takes time and patience – you will have to communicate again; tell him what pressure you like, where and how to move his tongue, which bits to suck on, where to blow softly. Teach him how to use his fingers inside you at the same time as licking your clitoris. And if you want really long sessions of oral sex then just hold his penis while he loves you; most men get to feel remote and cut off if there is no penile stimulation while they are loving you. If you hold them the energy is completing a circuit.

Bear in mind that during sex you have a role to play – as does your partner. Your role is to feed his energy so he can go on loving you for as long as you need. If he has an orgasm he may well find that the energy dissipates completely for a while and he will need to rest, perhaps even to sleep, to recover that energy. His role is to orchestrate and be active; your role is to participate and be creative. He worships your *Shakti*; you feed his *Shiva*. Without one, the other is lessened; together you are a powerful force. You will be able to maintain your levels of energy better if you are aware of your partner's need to orgasm and you should delay this as long as possible. If he is learning the lock method or the squeeze technique it's in your own best interests to help him as much as possible. Women often, quite rightly, complain that their lover is too quick, or doesn't spend enough time on foreplay; then they do everything in their power to make their lover orgasm quickly. It makes sense to help them delay the male orgasm. You will be able to have as many as you like and, each time you do, you are feeding their energy. Once they have ejaculated their energy level plummets. If they are learning and practising the ejaculateless orgasm you will together be able to reach new heights of pleasure.

Summary

In this chapter we have learnt how to prepare ourselves and our environment for good sex. We have learnt how to respect our space and that of our partner. We explored each other's sexuality in a safe and caring way without pressure or a need to 'perform'.

We have learnt various practical assignments including the tantric yoga relaxation positions. This enables us to explore how the energy moves in our bodies and how it relates to our partner's energy flow. We also learnt the position known as 'yab yum' and how this is widely used in tantric sex practices and how it can bring you and your partner closer together.

We explored tantric kissing and tantric skin exploration and how these help us to experience the flow of our energy and our partner's. We also explored our partner's orgasm through various assignments and began to appreciate the flow of energy through the *kundalini* – the serpent pathway.

We practised different ways of thrusting and learned about female ejaculation.

09

tantric sex positions

In this chapter you will learn:
- the 23 basic positions of the *Kama Sutra*
- positions from the *Ananga Ranga*
- positions from the *Perfumed Garden.*

It is not only that a man could nurture his Yang by taking Yin essence from the woman. A woman could also take Yang essence from the man to nurture her.

Chung Ho Tzu, 6th-century Chinese Taoist

In this chapter we will look at how the three great 'sacred sex' traditions – Hindu, Arabic and Taoist – looked at the positions for good sex. These positions weren't described and recommended for titillation or to teach lovers how to be contortionists; they were there for lovers to experiment with and to find positions that were comfortable so they could enjoy each other's energy for a long time. They were also described so that lovers could find positions where they could embrace and caress each other better or more intimately. These positions may seem to be about sex but they are actually more about love; you have to have a loving and trusting partner to work through these positions.

Let's begin by looking at the *Kama Sutra*. This ancient Hindu text suggests that there are 64 different lovemaking positions. On closer inspection it turns out that there are only 23, as each position has many variations depending on how deep the *lingam* – penis – is thrust into the *yoni* – vulva – or the manner in which it is moved. The *Kama Sutra* also deals in some depth with oral sex, which we will look at in a moment.

The 23 basic positions of the *Kama Sutra*

Positions with the man behind

The Congress of the Cow
The word *congress* is used in the *Kama Sutra* for *intercourse* or, more properly, *meeting*. In the Congress of the Cow, the couple should have sex in the manner brought to mind by the title of this position. The woman stands upright and bends forward until her hands touch the ground. The man then enters her from behind and clasps her around the waist, much as a bull would mount a cow. In this position he can also stimulate her clitoris and his pelvic bone will be able to stimulate the area around her buttocks and perineum.

Positions with the couple standing up

The Congress of the Vine (or the Supported Congress)
Here the couple have sex standing up with the man leaning back against a wall for support. To make entry easier the woman should entwine one of her legs around the back of the man's thighs. If the man is much taller, he should bend his knees and keep his legs apart so he can lower himself to the woman's level.

The Congress of the Monkey (or the Suspended Congress)
Here the man again leans back against a wall for support and the woman clasps him around the neck. She then springs up to put her legs around his hips and, simultaneously, he grips and supports her by her upper thighs or buttocks. By pushing her feet against the wall she can make a thrusting motion. Both this position and the preceding one need some strength and practice, but are good for spontaneous sex and indulging in erotic kissing.

Positions with the woman on top

The *Kama Sutra* says: 'Though a woman is reserved, and keeps her feelings hidden, when she mounts her man from above she can show all her love and desire, and from her actions a man should be able to tell what disposition she is in and in what way she likes to be enjoyed.'

The Pair of Tongs
This isn't so much a position as a technique to use when the man is lying down and the woman sits astride him, facing him. She then draws the *lingam* into her *yoni* using the PC muscle and, in the words of the *Kama Sutra*, 'presses it and keeps it thus in her for a long time'. The man, in this position, can caress the woman's breasts and she can stimulate her own clitoris – or the man can.

The Spinning Top
Here the couple begin as the Pair of Tongs, but the woman slowly, and carefully, swivels around until she is facing away from the man. This one is both difficult and potentially painful for the man. Take great care.

If the woman grips her partner's ankles she can then exert considerable pressure and friction on his *lingam* while still maintaining control. Some women find the Spinning Top quite tiring and some men find it painful because the woman's weight on the upper thighs can be restrictive. However, it is a fun position to try and can be very stimulating. Finally, the woman can swivel back again to face her partner.

The Swing
This is a variation on The Spinning Top. It simply requires the woman to swing her pelvis about in all directions as she slowly turns. The idea is to create sufficient stimulation to keep the man erect so she doesn't, as it were, fall off.

The Congress of The Mare
Again, this is more of a technique than a position and differs very little from The Pair of Tongs. It gets its name from the belief that a mare could actually 'catch' the *lingam* of a stallion using the lips of her *yoni*. Once it was inside, the mare was reputed to be able to hold it there as long as she liked. For a woman to do the same requires a very strong PC muscle.

Positions with the man on top

The Widely Opened Congress
Here the couple start in the 'man on top' position with the woman's knees outside his thighs. She should then arch her back and he should support his weight on his knees and arms. The woman's buttocks should not be in contact with whatever is underneath. The woman, by opening her legs as wide as possible, should be able to enjoy very deep penetration and good stimulation of her clitoris by the man's pelvic region.

The Yawning Congress
The woman lies down and raises and opens her legs as wide as possible. The man kneels between her legs and enters her. The couple should clasp hands to support each other's weight. The woman's inner thighs should grip around the man's waist.

The Highest Yawning Congress
The couple should take up the Yawning Congress and then the woman should bring her knees forward to rest on her breasts. The man can then straighten out his legs and take his weight on his arms. The woman can rest her feet on his shoulders. This position provides the deepest penetration.

The Congress of the Consort of Indra
Indra was the Hindu God of Thunder and this may have been his favourite position – or that of his consort or wife. The woman lies down on her back and brings her knees under her armpits, with her heels well clear of her *yoni* and as close to the bed as possible. The man kneels and enters her. In this position, he can stimulate her clitoris extremely well. For added tension she can grip her feet and pull them down onto the bed.

The Clasping Position
The woman lies down and the man enters her by lying on top of her. She entwines her legs with his and their arms also entwine. This position doesn't allow for much movement but it is a very intimate warm embrace.

The Side Clasping Position
The couple lie on their sides facing each other. The woman lifts one leg to allow the man to enter her. Again, they can entwine legs and arms or use their hands to caress each other.

The Twining Congress
The couple adopt the classic 'man on top' position. The woman should bring one leg around the back of her partner's thighs and draw him closer to her. At the same time she should clasp him around the neck and draw his head down to hers.

The Pressing Congress
The same as the Twining Congress but the woman uses both her legs to press even harder against his thighs. Her feet should grip quite hard behind his knees.

The Rising Congress
The woman should lie down on her back and draw her knees up to her breasts. The man kneels and enters her. He should then grip her legs and bring them up so that her feet are on his shoulders. He will need to open his thighs quite wide to enable him to penetrate her deeply. This position is quite tiring for the man, although it does afford the woman considerable pleasure due to its deep penetration.

The Pressed Congress
This one is very similar to the Congress of the Consort of Indra, but instead of the woman gripping her legs tightly to her she can relax her knees. The man can caress her feet and she can stroke his thighs.

The Half-Pressed Congress

Here the woman can relax one leg completely by stretching it out behind her partner. This lets him have access to her clitoris which he can then stimulate with his fingers.

The Nailed Half-Pressed Congress

From the previous position the woman can take the foot that is on the man's chest and lift her leg completely into the air. At the same time the man should extend one leg behind him.

The Congress of the Crab

The woman lies on her back with her legs wide apart and her knees drawn up. The man kneels and enters her. He clasps her knees to his chest. She can then let her legs down and draw them up again. If she does this quickly and smoothly he will gain a lot of pleasure from the tightening and relaxing of her *yoni*.

The Lotus Congress

The woman lies on her back with her knees drawn up and her calves crossed in an approximation of the famous yoga lotus position. The man enters kneeling. It's a position that opens the vagina and although he can't penetrate very deeply (because his partner's feet are in the way) it's a good posture for G-spot stimulation.

The Bamboo Congress

The man enters the woman who is lying on her back. She brings one leg up so that her foot is resting on his shoulder, while the other leg is stretched out. She then swaps over legs and by alternately raising and lowering a leg she can bring them both to orgasm. This one is supposed to resemble bamboo being split. It's not easy and really is only included so you can try it for fun.

The Turning Position

This, like The Spinning Top, is good for a laugh but is not to be taken seriously as a means of erotic stimulation. Beginning in The Clasping Position, the man gradually turns like the sail of a windmill so that he is sideways to his partner, then faces her feet, then faces sideways again, and finally returns to The Clasping Position once more. It requires a powerful erection otherwise the man is liable to slip out.

Movements of the *lingam*

Once these 23 positions have been mastered, or even during the learning process, the man can learn how to move his penis to afford the woman maximum satisfaction. The man's role is to satisfy the woman; unless you learn to be a patient, sympathetic and considerate lover you cannot attain the true tantra.

Movements of the *lingam* during lovemaking

The Moving Forward
The *lingam* is inserted into the *yoni* in a straightforward manner and pushed fully home.

The Sporting of the Sparrow
Here the *lingam* is moved in and out rapidly in tiny movements like a sparrow.

The Blows of the Bull and Bear
The *lingam* is rubbed against the side of the vaginal walls.

The Giving of a Blow
The *lingam* is used to strike the outside of the *yoni* – especially effective if struck against the clitoris.

The Pressing
The *lingam* is pushed as deeply as possible into the *yoni* and kept there – a good opportunity to stimulate the clitoris with fingers.

The Rubbing
This is inserting the *lingam* and pushing hard against the 'bottom' of the *yoni* – the vaginal wall on the opposite side to the clitoris.

The Piercing
This is the same as the Rubbing except the *lingam* is rubbed hard against the 'top' of the *yoni* – the vaginal wall where the G-spot is situated.

The Churning
The *lingam* is used inside the yoni and is 'churned' about rubbing against the vaginal walls.

You might like to experiment with your own variations of these – and invent names for them.

Oral sex

The *Kama Sutra* gives advice to a man on how to give oral sex to a woman – it says the man should follow the same advice as for kissing – refer to Chapter 08 for advice on tantric kissing.

For the woman there is some more helpful advice about oral sex. The *Kama Sutra* suggests that there is an eightfold path to *auparishtaka* or mouth congress:

- **Nominal Congress** – to begin with the *lingam* is caressed by the mouth.
- **Biting the Sides** – the *lingam* is held by the woman and her teeth can gently nibble along the sides.
- **Outside Pressing** – the head of the *lingam* is sucked gently by the lips.
- **Inside Pressing** – the whole of the *lingam* is inserted into the mouth and long deep sucks are given by the whole mouth.
- **Kissing** – the *lingam* is kissed all over by the woman.
- **Tonguing** – the *lingam* is fiercely licked all over by the woman's tongue.
- **Sucking the Mango Fruit** – about half of the *lingam* is inserted into the woman's mouth and she should suck hard in the same manner as the Inside Pressing.
- **Swallowing Up** – the whole of the *lingam* is taken into the mouth and sucked hard with a deep swallowing motion.

The Congress of the Crow
If the couple want to engage in mutual oral sex they should adopt the *Congress of the Crow*. This is the classic '69' position of Western sex practices. Here the couple can engage in mutual caressing of the genitals in comfort.

The *Ananga Ranga*

The *Ananga Ranga* only offers a few variations on the positions given in the *Kama Sutra*, but it does offer one excellent variation of the 'woman on top' position – that of the Position of the Large Bee.

The Large Bee Position
The woman sits astride the man with his *lingam* entered into her *yoni*. She closes her legs in front of her and grasps his *lingam* tightly. She can then lean back and take her own weight on her arms – even gripping his ankles with her hands if she wants to and it feels comfortable. She can then begin a series of twisting

movements from the waist down – this is the large bee. The advice given in the tantric text is that she shouldn't be too aggressive or masculine in her movements as it will upset her partner's ego. However, modern lovers shouldn't have to worry too much about that and the woman can let go to all her desires at this stage. Most women find this position extremely comfortable and they can maintain it for quite a long time.

The woman's orgasm
The woman may like to experiment by moving her legs forwards or backwards until the optimum position for comfort and friction is found. Basically, the man has to lie back and enjoy his partner doing all the work. As a man you might like to thrust your hips upwards at the same time as your partner moves her waist from side to side. The man can caress his partner's breasts and she can stimulate her clitoris at the same time. If the simultaneous orgasm is important to you both then this is probably the best position to achieve it. The woman can bring herself to clitoral orgasm at the same time as the man ejaculates and she should be able to control the speed and pace much more sensitively in this position.

If the woman has mastered the yonic squeeze technique (PC muscle) then she may well be able to bring her partner to orgasm without moving any part of her body except her *yoni*.

The *Perfumed Garden*

There are 11 main lovemaking positions featured in the *Perfumed Garden*. Some of them are variations on ones we have already described from the *Kama Sutra*. They are simply described as *Manner the First*, *Manner the Second* and so forth. The *Perfumed Garden* does say that the positions that the Indian peoples use are more varied and better and goes on to describe them, which we will look at in a bit.

The 11 main lovemaking positions in the *Perfumed Garden*

Manner the First
The woman lies down on her back with her thighs raised. The man kneels between her legs and 'introduces his member into her'. He presses his toes into the ground and can then 'rummage her in a convenient, measured way'. This position is said to be gentle for the woman whose partner has a 'long measure'.

Manner the Second

The woman lies on her back, lifts her legs into the air and brings her legs as near to her head as she can. The man then kneels and enters her. This position is said to be good if the man has a 'short measure' as it will afford the woman a degree of satisfaction.

Manner the Third

The woman lies down and the man enters her from the kneeling position. She raises one leg only over his shoulder. This position will enable the couple to enjoy really deep penetration.

Manner the Fourth

The woman lies down and the man enters her from the kneeling position. He then raises her legs up so that they are over his shoulders and he can grip her thighs as he thrusts deeply.

Manner the Fifth

Both partners lie down on their sides facing each other. This position is good for generating feelings of warmth and love; it is very intimate.

Manner the Sixth

The woman kneels on all fours and then lowers her head to the ground. The man kneels behind her and enters her.

Manner the Seventh

The woman lies on her side and the man squats between her thighs with one of her legs on his shoulders and the other between his thighs. The man can then draw her to him by using his hands.

Manner the Eighth

The woman lies down on her back with her legs crossed at the knees. The man sits astride her like 'a cavalier on horseback' and, being on his knees, can 'put his member into her'.

Manner the Ninth

The woman kneels forward being propped up on a bed or raised couch. The man kneels behind her and enters her from behind. The man can keep his legs either side of hers.

Manner the Tenth

The woman half-lies on a low couch so that the bottom half of her body is unsupported. The man kneels in front of her and enters her. She can then use her legs around his waist to support her and he can lean forward and grip the low couch for support.

Manner the Eleventh

The woman lies down on her back with a cushion under her buttocks. The man lies astride her and enters her; she should then cross her ankles over just behind and below his knees – or she can bring her feet together, sole to sole.

The 25 superior Indian lovemaking positions

The *Perfumed Garden* then goes on to describe the 25 positions of Indian lovemaking which, it claims, are superior to the Arabic tradition.

These are the 25 further positions of the *Perfumed Garden*, which does state that these shouldn't be tried by ill or unfit couples.

The Stopperage

The woman lies on her back with a cushion under her buttocks and the man enters her from the front. He should keep his legs outstretched and she should bend her legs up so that her knees are on his chest. The *Perfumed Garden* says this position can be uncomfortable for the woman and should only really be tried if the man's member is short or soft.

Frog Fashion

The woman lies on her back with her knees raised but her feet flat on the floor. The man sits with his legs around her sides. He enters her and holds on with his hands to her shoulders. Her knees should be under the man's armpits.

With the Toes Cramped

The woman lies on her back and the man kneels and enters her from the front. He should then grip with his toes and pull her up off the ground so that her buttocks can swing freely onto the front of his thighs. Her legs can then cross behind his back and he can grip her neck with his hands.

With Legs in the Air

The woman lies on her back and the man kneels and enters her from the front. Her legs should then be supported on his shoulders and he can lean forward.

He-Goat Fashion

The woman lies on her side and she stretches out the leg that is underneath. The man squats down between her thighs with his calves bent under him. He then lifts her uppermost leg so that it rests on his back and enters her. During this position he can take hold of the woman by her shoulders for extra leverage.

The Screw Of Archimedes

The man lies down on his back and the woman sits on him, facing him. She should then lean forward and take her weight on her arms positioned either side of his head. She can then slide up and down his member and, if he is agile, he can assist her by moving as well.

The Somersault

This one really is only for the very supple and very agile. The woman lies on her back with her legs up – with one foot placed either side of her head and the man lies along her and enters her. It's called the somersault because it was originally recommended that to get into this position the woman should wear a pair of *pantaloons* which she should drop so that they fitted around her ankles. She should then bend forward and put her head in them and the man should then seize her legs and somersault her into this position.

The Tail of the Ostrich

The woman lies on her back and the man kneels in front of her and lifts up her legs until only her head and shoulders remain in contact with the ground. He then enters her, from behind, and straightens his back so that he is kneeling upright. She can then cross her ankles behind his head.

Fitting on of the Sock

The man kneels down and the woman lies with her legs open and either side of his waist. He can lean back on his calves. He should then be able to use his member to stimulate the area around her vulva. In this position he can use his fingers to stimulate her clitoris as well. The *Perfumed Garden* says: 'When her vulva gets moistened with the liquid emitted from his verge she is thus amply prepared for enjoyment by the alternate coming and going of your weapon in her scabbard; put it into her in full length.'

Reciprocal Sight of the Posteriors

The man lies stretched out on his back and the woman sits down on his member with her back to him. He can press the outside of her thighs between his thighs and legs while she places her hands on the ground as a support.

The Rainbow Arch

The woman lies on her side with one leg raised. The man lays also on his side with his face towards her back. He then enters her and keeps his hands on her back. She can then reach forward and grip his feet and bring them forwards towards her front forming him into an arch.

The Alternate Movement of Piercing

The man sits with his legs outstretched and the woman sits in his lap. He then draws his legs up under her thighs and she grips his back with her legs. He should hold her round the waist and she can support herself by leaning back on her arms. All he has to do then is move his feet together to provide all the movement and friction they will require.

Pounding on the Spot

The same basic position as the Alternate Movement of Piercing except the man keeps his legs stretched out and the woman grips him tighter round the back.

Coitus from the Back

The woman lies face down and the man enters her from behind. He should keep his legs outstretched and inside hers. She should place a cushion or pillow under her so that her buttocks are raised.

Belly to Belly

The couple stand facing each other. He brings one leg forward and she raises one leg. He should then be able to enter her quite easily. Both partners should have their arms around each other's hips.

After the Fashion of the Ram

The woman is on her knees with her forearms on the ground. The man kneels behind her and enters her and places his hands on her shoulders.

Driving the Peg Home

The woman leans back against a wall and the man enters her from the front. She takes her weight on her back and raises her legs, which she should lock around the back of his thighs. She can give herself additional support by holding onto his shoulders. He can then 'drive the peg home'.

Love's Fusion

While the woman is lying on her right side, the man should lay on his left with his left leg extended. The man's right leg should be raised until it is up to her flank, when he then lays her upper leg on his side. The *Perfumed Garden* then says: 'After having introduced your member you move as you please, and she responds to your action as she pleases.'

Coitus of the Sheep

The woman is on her hands and knees; the man, behind her, lifts her thighs until her vulva is on a level with his member, which he then inserts. In this position she ought to place her head between her arms.

Interchange in Coition

The man lies on his back. The woman, gliding in between his legs, places herself upon him with her toenails against the ground. She lifts up the man's thighs so he can enter her. She can then take her weight on her hands which she places either side of the man's body. The *Perfumed Garden* says this is an exact opposite of our traditional 'missionary position' and that a variation is for the woman to kneel with her legs under her but between his legs.

The Race of the Member

The man, on his back, supports himself with a cushion under his shoulders but with his buttocks on whatever is underneath him. He then draws up his thighs until his knees are on a level with his face. The woman then sits on him, 'impaling herself on his member; she must not lie down but keep seated as if on horseback, the saddle being represented by the knees and the stomach of the man'. All she has to do then is jog up and down by flexing her knees to bring them both to orgasm.

The Fitter In

The man sits with his legs apart and the woman sits between them. He enters her and they grip each other's elbows or forearms. Her legs should be around his waist and all four feet should be on the ground. They can then rock gently back and forth.

The One Who Stops At Home

The woman lies down on her back with her shoulders and upper back supported by cushions. She arches her back and brings her feet back so that her knees are raised. She opens her legs and the man can half-kneel and enter her. She then raises and drops her buttocks to provide excitement and friction, but the man has to follow her movements or his member will become dislodged – he has to 'stick like glue to her'.

The Coition of the Blacksmith

The woman lies on her back with a cushion under her buttocks and her knees raised as far as possible towards her chest so that her vulva stands out as a target. She then guides her partner's member in. He then 'executes for some time coition in the usual manner then draws his tool out of the vulva, and glides it for a moment between the thighs of the woman, as the smith withdraws the glowing iron from the furnace in order to plunge it into cold water'.

The Seducer

The woman lies on her back and the man sits between her legs. She can then draw her legs up around his shoulders and guide his member in. She can clasp her legs around his waist if that is more comfortable.

Positions from the *Tao*

The Chinese tantric texts give all the positions that we have so far looked at, but really only divide positions into four kinds: man on top, woman on top, couple side by side (and face to face) and man from behind. They called these *Yang Superior*, *Yin Superior*, *Intimate Attachment* and *Fish Sunning Itself*. They suggested that lovemaking should be fluid and versatile, there being no set positions – the lovers just moving smoothly from one position to the next without there being any moment when they could be said to be in any one position. The Taoists also recognized the fact that all couples are physically different and that what one couple can do another may not physically be able to manage. They understand that there might be false expectations or disappointment if someone couldn't manage something; they might feel that they had somehow 'failed'.

The Taoist positions

The *Tao of Loving* describes 26 basic positions, all of which we have covered; but the Taoists had such interesting names for their positions it's worth looking at a few.

A Phoenix Plays in a Red Cave
The woman, Lady Yin, lies on her back and holds her legs upright with her hands and Lord Yang enters her.

Bamboo Near the Altar
The couple face each other standing up – Intimate Attachment – and the man enters the woman. They can grip on wherever they feel comfortable.

The Springing White Tiger
The woman kneels forward and the man kneels behind her. He enters her and she should drop forward so that her head is touching the ground.

Dragon Faces the Mountain
The man sits in a chair and the woman sits in his lap with her back to him.

Flying Birds on a Dark Sea
The woman lies on a raised platform or bed with her legs over the side. The man stands and enters her and holds her legs up. A variation on this is the *Flying Seagull* where the couch or bed is much lower and the man kneels.

The Taoist names

Some of the Taoist terminology is wonderful – we have the *Jade Hammer*, the *Heavenly Dragon Stem*, the *Red Phoenix* and the *Coral Stalk* for penis. The *Jade Pavilion* and *Palace*, the *Open Lotus Flower* and the *Red Valley* for the vulva. The clitoris is the *Jade Pearl* and the *Golden Jewel of the Jade Palace*. Sex is *Mist on the Mountains of Wu* and the *Meeting of the Dragon and the Unicorn* or even just the *Clouds and the Rain*. An orgasm is the *Bursting of the Clouds*.

The three parts of sex

In the West we tend to divide sex up into three distinct parts – the *seduction*, the *sex* and the *afterglow*. In the East the tantric texts suggested that sex is something that goes on indefinitely – there is no distinction between the three phases – they are all going on all the time; we just fail to see that. If we hold that in mind our lovemaking becomes even more erotic. Even when we are having sex we should be seducing, arousing, caressing and loving. There will be moments during sex when we will stop to rest and then we can experience that afterglow but, in between, when we are arousing and seducing, we can be having sex with our eyes and fingertips. If the energy is universal we can be enjoying any part of it at any time and in any way we want to. The proverb at the beginning of this chapter has its equivalent in Taoism: 'A loving glance from our heart's desire brings us closer to Heaven's rain than a thousand nights of wasted ching.'

A deeper need

The whole point of tantric sexuality is that it promotes sex from being a mere pleasure activity to being one of great spiritual significance. All the ancient texts agreed that spirituality was a 24-hour-a-day pursuit: 'Let every act be a service, let every service be worship, let every worship be continuous' (Chu Lin, a Taoist teacher, 4th century CE). If sex is a perfect representation of our love, not only for our partner but also for the Universal Principle, then we should be in love continually. That love can be expressed in a glance, a gesture, a touch, a kiss, a stroke of the hair. These moments are the acts of service, the worship, and they can be as electric as an orgasm. Sometimes we need that love, that closeness to the Universal Principle, and we make the mistake of thinking that our need for sex is that love; if we could separate our feelings we might be happier to be close to our lover in a warm and intimate embrace than having quick and unsatisfactory sex. The need for sexual gratification is often taken, in the West, for being exactly that – a need for instant gratification. But there is a deeper need that should be fulfilled. Tantric sex is about using sex to fulfil that deeper need. Our sex life becomes infinitely more varied and exciting if we recognize that we aren't just *having sex* but also exchanging energy, worshipping the Universal Principle, experiencing an intimacy and closeness with another human being, nurturing our inner self, acting out our karma, and even exploring the universe beyond the confines of our bodies. All in all quite a package.

If it feels good, do it

In this multipurpose activity there can be nothing you can do that is wrong – providing you are doing it together with mutual consent and participation. In the West there are many barriers to sex and a lot of preconceived notions about what is right or wrong, good or bad, decent or indecent, moral or immoral, nice or not nice, tasteful or distasteful. None of this is true about sex. There is what there is. If it feels good – do it. If it feels wrong – then don't. Sex can only enhance your spirituality – it can never detract from it. Sex is an act of supreme worship. If the sex is tacky or distasteful, hurried or forbidden, then that is the level of your worship. And remember – *as you sow so shall you reap*. If your acts of worship are open, loving, relaxed, satisfactory and clear then the Universal Principle will respond in a like manner. If your acts of worship are furtive and guilt-ridden, abusive and badly motivated then how can you expect the Universal Principle to respond positively?

Two notions about sex

There are two notions about sex still prevalent in the West that haven't changed in many hundreds of years. One is that, for men, sex is something to be got in large quantities and that quality doesn't enter into it. The second is that for women to enjoy their sexuality openly and freely somehow makes them not nice. Neither notion could be further from the truth, but both notions seem to show no signs of departing as rapidly as they should. For men, once they have had it proved that quality is much more important than quantity, they come to realize that sex within a loving, committed, trusting relationship is far more satisfactory and much more sustaining than they would have thought possible. For women, once they have managed to battle against a thousand hidden social signals that somehow sex is not nice for a woman to enjoy, they come to realize that they are as fully sexually charged as men and entitled to express that sexuality as openly and as freely as they want. 'Men have to learn to step back, women to step forward' (Chu Lin).

Taking the best

Part of the problem with the two notions just discussed is that the old tantric texts were written by men, for male-dominated societies. We have to take what is best from them and discard the rest – the old outdated stuff. We live in a modern, potentially liberated, society where we can explore sexuality in a much freer environment. But we've a long way to go yet.

Making allowances

In remainder of this chapter we will look at seduction, erotica, foreplay, intimacy, afterglow and prolonging the mood – and our enjoyment of every single one of these is influenced by how far we have come from those two notions. Now I'm not suggesting that you, dear reader, suffer from either – but your lover may and you have to make allowances.

Seduction

We can wear whatever we like to please our lover. We can phone them and make suggestive remarks. We can caress them secretly, intimately, in public. We can expose our bodies to our lover in whatever manner we want. We can take the initiative in suggesting sexual positions or foreplay. We can choose when, where and how we make love.

The important aspects of seduction

How many of the aspects just mentioned do you feel comfortable with? It's not a test. Seduction is about getting ourselves and our lover ready for making love. It's not about seducing new lovers, that's something different. If we are getting ourselves ready we have to think ahead. We have to be considerate and know what the other likes, wants and needs – and we have to be prepared to give it. That doesn't mean we have to do anything we don't want to, or find objectionable or distasteful. It means we have to be considerate of their sexual needs and proclivities; and our own, of course. We have to know how our lover responds to us sexually and we to them – and this all means communication. If we don't talk about it we won't know. If we don't pick up the signals, we'll remain in the dark. The three most important aspects of seduction are: atmosphere, idea and inclination.

The right atmosphere

We have to provide the right atmosphere. The room for making love should be prepared in advance – and if your dream is to have savage and wonderfully wanton sex on the kitchen table (and yes, you are allowed to under the rule of tantric sex that anything you want is permissible) then you might need to clear away the dirty dishes and make sure the table is sturdy enough! There are many couples whose lovemaking goes wildly awry through lack of planning.

The idea

We have to implant the idea. A whispered suggestion can be more seductive than an open invitation because most sex goes on in the lover's head. The idea is very important. A tiny hint of what is to come later is a bit like reading the menu in a restaurant – it whets the appetite and gets the juices flowing.

The inclination

The inclination has to be there. If you provide the first two then the third will undoubtedly follow. If it doesn't, you can help it along by knowing your partner's needs. If your partner is never very sexy first thing in the morning and you want desperately to make love when you are half-waking up then you could always suggest an afternoon nap (or whatever time they are particularly 'in the mood'). You'll get your wish and they will be happy to oblige without having to force anything. Plan ahead and use what you know about them to satisfy both of you.

Erotica

The Japanese *shunga* or 'spring drawings' as well as the Chinese pillow books contain explicit pictures of people making love in all sorts of positions and places; they are very erotic. They were designed to help couples know what was available and how to participate. They weren't designed to titillate or provide single males with fantasies. They were for couples.

The centrefold syndrome

Modern erotica falls woefully short of that sort of sophistication. Recent research done at the University of California by Dr Deborah Then has highlighted a modern condition – the *centrefold syndrome*. This is where men become unsatisfied with their partners because they don't look like *Playboy* centrefolds. Unfortunately, centrefolds are not 'normal'; they have had breast implants, substantial 'air brushing' and myriad other tweaks and tricks of the trade to make them more glamorous and 'sexy'. But they can make men feel unhappy with real women – 75 per cent of the men questioned by Dr Then said that they wanted the women in their lives to look like centrefolds and many said that they didn't think it caused problems.

God's a bit fat too

Because of the vast amounts of pornography, men's magazines and such like that is available today in the West, men may all be unconsciously guilty of the centrefold syndrome to a greater or lesser extent. And the same seems to be happening to women. They too suffer from a need for their partners to have the *Calvin Klein look*. If your lover is a perfect representation of the Universal Principle then perhaps you just have to accept that the Universal Principle has wobbly bits.

Foreplay

The whispered suggestion that we mentioned under 'seduction' is the start of foreplay. Good foreplay is as important as good sex – it's providing the atmosphere, the idea and the inclination. Too often it's rushed as if it's something to be got through before the main course. But it can *be* the main course. Once we lose the Western orgasm goal focus we can enjoy foreplay until it becomes 'all play'. How many lovers have you known who, as soon as penetrative sex takes place, stop tweaking and touching all those sensitive bits that they were touching beforehand? How many lovers think that a quick bit of fondling will 'get them in the mood'? How wrong are they? Foreplay should be continuous throughout sex – and afterwards. Foreplay is all the best bits – the licking and kissing, the fondling and caressing, the touching and stroking, the tasting and nibbling, the smelling and teasing, the rubbing and scratching, the tweaking and biting, the sucking and arousing. Need I say more?

Intimacy

Sex is the closest we will ever get to each other; inside each other and around each other. If we trust another to be that close we have to be *intimate* with them. Intimate comes from the Latin *intermatum* – within. And that's where we should be with our lover – within. Within their hearts and minds and souls. That's the beauty of tantric sexuality – it teaches us about respect.

When we respect the person we are making love with, then we can be truly intimate with them because we trust them with our inner selves as well – and then we can let go and be truly open. When we are intimate with our lover and partner, we are opening ourselves not only to them but also to that energy, that Universal Principle. Then we can be filled with that energy. If we are closed we cannot receive anything.

Afterglow

After sex, afterglow. That is the time for warmth and companionship, for holding and being close to our lover. Not for getting up and going off to watch television, for falling asleep or for going home to our spouse. Afterglow is for bathing in, for recharging the energy, for holding and comforting, for re-establishing ourselves in that love, for getting our breath back so we are ready again to please our lover, for enjoying our lover's satisfaction and contentment. Afterglow is for glowing in afterwards. Don't hurry it, enjoy.

Prolonging the mood

The Taoists say that if you let the fires of sexual energy dwindle too low then you have to relight them all over again – but if you blow on the embers the fire will flare up again quickly. During the afterglow you can continue caressing and touching and then you will prolong the mood. And then the afterglow will become seduction, and the seduction foreplay and your sexuality will be continuous – and you'll be truly tantric.

Homosexual tantric sex

If you are in a gay relationship, please feel free to adopt any of the principles in this book for your own sexuality. The tantric texts didn't cover gay sex to a great extent; however, any two people who are in a loving, trusting, relationship can practise tantric sex no matter what sex they are. Tantric sex is about using sex as a means of enhancing our spirituality and that Universal Principle embraces all of us no matter what path we followed to get there.

Summary

In this chapter we looked at and explored the three great tantric traditions – Hindu, Arabic and Taoist. These traditions enable us to enhance our performance and teach us how to become better lovers. They teach us the 'skill' of sex so we can keep going longer and give our partner better pleasure.

We began with the 23 basic positions of the *Kama Sutra* and then moved on to the *Ananga Ranga* which only gives one main additional position – the Position of the Large Bee. We then explored the *Perfumed Garden* and the 11 main lovemaking positions. These are the positions from the Arabic tradition and we followed these with the 25 Hindu positions which are also described in the *Perfumed Garden*. We are told that the Arabic tradition claims that these are 'superior' to the previous ones. We than explored the sexual positions from the Taoist tradition.

All these positions should be used when and as you feel you want to use them. They don't have to be done as a ritual but rather as a fun and pleasurable part of sex.

We explored various ideas about sex, such as the way sex in the West is viewed differently from the way it is viewed in the East.

We also learnt to make allowances for our partner's (and our own, of course) performance and we looked at the importance of seduction, foreplay, intimacy and how to prolong the mood.

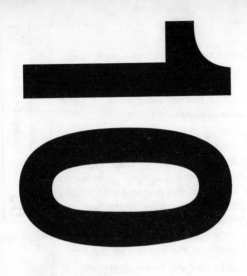

10
the origins of tantric sex

In this chapter you will learn:
- the difference between traditional and 'neo' tantra
- traditional tantric practices
- how tantric sex came to the West

*There is but one thing which all seek – happiness –
though it be of differing kinds and sought in different
ways. All forms, whether sensual, intellectual, or
spiritual, are from the Brahman, who is Itself the Source
and Essence of all Bliss, and Bliss itself... and thus it is
said that man can never be truly happy until he seeks
shelter with Brahman, which is Itself the great Bliss.*

Arthur Avalon (Sir John Woodroffe), *Introduction
to the Mahanirvana Tantra*

Tantric sex, as described in this book, is a modern, Western
adaptation of an Eastern tradition that goes back thousands of
years. Now that you know all about the way tantric sex is
practised today in Europe and the USA you might like to know
more about its origins. It's a fascinating subject and the deeper
you go into it the more you'll get out of tantric sex and,
indeed, life.

Neo-tantric sex and traditional
tantric sex

Some people say that the way we practise tantric sex in the West
should really be called neo-tantra (that's to say, 'new-tantra') to
distinguish it from the traditional forms. And it's true that to
talk of 'tantric sex' can be confusing because there are still
people today, especially in parts of India and even in North
America and the UK, who practise a very different style of
tantric sex based on the traditional rituals.

The first thing to emphasize is that traditional tantric sex is only
one part of a much wider system of beliefs and practices called
Tantra, most of which have absolutely nothing to do with sex.
Tantra is often described as a 'cult of ecstasy' or something like
that. But, in fact, you could be a follower of Tantra without ever
having any sex at all. Sex is actually forbidden to those who are
not considered 'ready'. Tantra defies precise definition but you
could say it's simply a range of practices for experiencing the
'divine energy'. Traditional tantric techniques include the
repetition of *mantras* (words that cause particularly special
vibrations) and meditating on *yantras* (energy diagrams). And,
yes, they also could include tantric sex.

The difference between 'traditional tantric sex' and 'neo-tantric sex' is this:

- 'Traditional tantric sex' is concerned with the union of one or both participants with the divine energy for the purpose of *enlightenment*.
- Modern Western tantric sex is mostly concerned with the divine union of the two participants with one another for the purpose of *pleasure* (although, as we've seen, an experience of God could also come into it).

In other words, in traditional tantric ritual, a sexual partner is nothing more than a vehicle for helping to achieve enlightenment. You could make love with your regular partner as a way of achieving that but you could equally have sex with somebody you've never even met before. Sex is merely a tool in exactly the same way that a rope is a tool for climbing a mountain. You might prefer to have your real life partner as your climbing partner on the other end of the rope but it certainly isn't essential. The important thing is the rope and the skill in using it.

Practical assignment: A taste of traditional tantra

So let's get a taste of this different traditional style of tantric sex. We're going to be going into a lot more detail in the rest of the chapter. For now, let's try the exercise of having sex without giving thought either to our partner or to pleasure but exclusively to the Divine Consciousness.

Try positions in which your only contact is through the genitals. The reason for that is that it then becomes easier to concentrate on the spiritual aspect. In 'Manner the Sixth' of the *Perfumed Garden*, for example, (popularly known as 'doggy style') the man just has to lean back a little, away from his partner, for you both to become physically and mentally detached. The man can throw his head right back to stare at the ceiling while the woman can close her eyes or stare ahead. You can see this in quite a lot of Indian erotic art. There are those paintings in which there is the 'meeting of the eyes' and then there are those others – in the spirit of traditional Tantra – in which the man and woman are looking away from one another, usually up to the sky and always with a serene but other-worldly expression. Now contemplate the meaning of life, the secret of the universe and God.

The history of Tantra

Nobody knows exactly how or when Tantra arose. Tantra doesn't have a founder as Islam and Christianity do. We can only say that some of the ideas underpinning Tantra have been around for thousands of years. They were certainly a formal, identifiable body of beliefs by around the seventh century CE because the earliest surviving Tantric texts are thought to date from then (although some scholars date them in the ninth or tenth centuries). Those early surviving texts were, in fact, Buddhist texts but most people think Tantra arose in India out of or parallel with Hinduism. From India it probably spread to Tibet during the seventh century, China during the eighth century (and from there to Japan) and to Cambodia and Java in the ninth century. And, eventually, it came to the West.

In fact, there are elements of Tantra to be found in the *Vedas* and in the *Upanishads*, which are the seminal texts of the Hindu religion. So that seems to support the case for India. The four *Vedas* are some of the most ancient books in the world, probably written down between 1500 and 500 BCE, while the various *Upanishads* were written between, maybe, 800 BCE and 1400 CE. *Veda* simply means 'knowledge' while *Upanishads* conveys the idea of 'learning at the feet of a master'. I say the *Vedas* were 'written down' because Hindus believe they are *shruti*, that is to say, revealed texts that have always existed (*apaurusheya*). That's right, always. Not from the beginning of the Earth or the beginning of the universe but *always*. They were not written by prophets but heard by *rishis* (seers) during meditation and written down.

The *Vedas* 'explain' the origin of the universe. And rather beautifully, too. They say that there was neither what is nor what is not. That darkness was hidden in darkness. But in that infinite peace, the ONE was breathing by its own power. And in the ONE, love arose.

That's fairly straightforward. But the problem with the *Vedas* and the *Upanishads* is that they were written in 'poetic' language in which everything has a mystical as well as a surface meaning. In other words, they were often allegories. And the Tantras are just the same. So it's very difficult to understand them and pin down exactly what they're telling us.

What would you make of this, for example? It comes from the *Vishvasara Tantra*:

What is here is elsewhere; what is not here is nowhere.

In fact, that's one puzzle we can solve fairly easily. The universe consists of a *Mahabrahmanda* or Grand Cosmos and of numerous *Brihatbrahmanda* or macrocosms evolved from it. In other words, you're a *Brihatbrahmanda*. So am I. The entire universe is contained within each of us. What is here, within us, is also elsewhere, in the rest of the universe. If it's not within us then it doesn't exist.

Practical assignment: Writing in riddles

Why not try writing to your partner in this allegorical style? Instead of directly saying what you want, hide the meaning in the way of the *Vedas*, *Upanishads* and *Tantras*. It would be fun, for example, to conceal a sexy message in a sort of code. Why? Because someone who discovers a meaning is usually more strongly affected and remembers it better. Try this for example: 'He who would leave the highway to take the narrow path must expect to travel more slowly.' Or: 'The gate to a castle is not taken by force but by gentleness.' What's that all about? Well, anal sex. You work it out.

Tantra under British rule

When India was invaded by Muslims, Tantra had to change or go underground. Muslims, like Hindus, were very happy with the idea of sex for pleasure but it had to be between married couples only. Moreover, to avoid temptation, women had to be kept out of the way and covered from head to foot. Then came the British with the notion that advanced, modern people really didn't have sex at all, except for procreation. So Tantra changed yet again. The problem is that most of the Tantric texts available in English were written during the Victorian period and are tainted with puritanism. One famous Tantric scholar, Jaganmohana Tarkalamkara, wrote a commentary to the Mahanirvana Tantra in the following terms: 'Let us consider what most contributes to the fall of man, making him forget his duty, sink into sin and die an early death. First among these are wine and women...' Whoops! That doesn't exactly sound like the Tantra we thought we knew. So which is the 'real' Tantra? Well, that's just the point. There isn't any longer one Tantra.

There are various different 'schools' of Tantra and, if you're interested, you'll have to choose the one that suits you the best.

The elements of traditional Tantra

According to Tantric (and Hindu) belief, the Divine Consciousness has always existed and will always exist. It has no beginning and no end. The ONE or the Divine Consciousness, which for convenience is pictured as a male god and given the name Shiva, was lonely. So Shiva created Shakti, the female. That was the moment the visible universe came into being and everything in it works on that same principle of opposites. Male and female, positive and negative, matter and anti-matter, wet and dry, hot and cold and so on. And pure and impure. In other words, even evil is a manifestation of the divine.

So one aspect of Tantra is the embracing of things that society considered to be taboo. In Hindu Tantra that meant the ritual use of wine, meat, fish, parched grain and sexual intercourse in a group. These things came to be known as the 'five Ms' because, in Sanskrit, each of them begins with the letter 'M'. Equally, during ceremonies, people broke taboos to mingle without regard to caste or sex.

Practical assignment: Breaking taboos

None of the 'five Ms' are taboo in our society other than group or public sex. So if you want to celebrate the dynamism of the universe you're going to have to find some other 'forbidden fruits' that you can symbolically enjoy.

In the context of a loving relationship you wouldn't want to have sex together with other people. But what about your personal taboos? What about anal stimulation and anal sex, for example? If that's been a personal taboo of yours then maybe you should consider introducing it into your tantric ritual. What about sex toys? If you've always been against them then see Chapter 11. And if you've never seen a porn film then that's something to consider. Making love at the same time as other couples, albeit on DVD/video, was an aspect of traditional Tantra.

Maya

Followers of Tantra believe our inability to apprehend the Divine Consciousness is due to something called *maya*. The concept of *maya* is often explained by saying that what we see is an illusion. But that's not quite right. A better analogy is of a light enclosed by something. If it's glass the brilliance is hardly affected, if it's paper the light is dimmer and if it's enclosed in metal no light can be seen at all. All such coverings are *maya* but for the people who live in the 'mayik world' the coverings are real enough, not illusions. According to the *Mahanirvana Tantra*, there is no bond equal in strength to *maya*, and no force greater to destroy that bond than yoga which, as we'll see, can be used in Tantra.

Traditional Tantra in practice

Ritual sex was only one part of traditional Tantra. Depending on the 'school' of Tantra it might have been a large part or it might have played hardly any part at all. There are plenty of other aspects to Tantric practice other than sex. Here are a few words and practices explained.

The guru

A guru is a religious teacher and spiritual guide. There is no question of buying a book and learning everything from that alone. A guru is essential.

Practical assignment: Finding a guru

Ideally, a guru wouldn't be found by looking in any kind of directory, you should go to India and wander. They say that when the moment is right the guru appears. They also say that only he who is fit for a teacher is able to recognize him or her.

But in the rest of the world you might never encounter a guru by chance so take a look at Chapter 12, Taking it further. Given that there are so many different kinds of Tantra, make sure your guru teaches the style you want.

If you become a disciple you'll be a *shishya* and your relationship with your guru will continue until *siddhi* or success. Another word for you would be a *sadhaka*, which is someone who performs all the necessary *sadhanas* or rites.

The reason that only a guru can achieve special things is that, in fact, he or she is – at such times – nothing other than the mouthpiece of the 'Supreme Guru' who, ultimately, is God. In other words, it's actually the Supreme Guru who is instructing you, through the voice of the earthly guru. That is why, in some sects, a guru is treated *as* a god.

Puja

Puja means worship and is the root of Indian ceremonial. A deity is invited into a special image and there are then 16 special things to be done (known as *upachara*), including providing food, water for drinking, water for washing the feet, burning incense and offering prayers. In Tantra, a *pujari* may make *puja* to *yoni* symbols or to a symbolic *lingam*. Or the deities may be invited into the participants themselves so that they 'become' gods for a while, which is exactly what happens during ritual sex. During *puja*, ritual gestures known as *mudra* are used. The *yoni-mudra*, for example, represents the *yoni* by using the two thumbs, the two first fingers and the two little fingers.

Practical assignment: Your partner as a god or goddess

You may already think your partner is pretty special. Hopefully you do. In this exercise, you're going to think of your partner as even more than that. Think of him or her as a god or goddess. Dwell on the enormity of what you're going to do, you're going to have sex with a deity. You can underline it by actually saying so. Something like, 'you are the god Shiva and this is the *lingam* of the god Shiva' or 'you are the goddess Shakti and this is the *yoni* of the goddess Shakti'. But don't forget that you're a deity as well. In Tantra, the divine is within all of us.

Yantra

A *yantra* in its most general sense is any instrument by which something is accomplished. Here we're concerned with *yantras* as sort of abstract designs. I say 'sort of' because although they may look a little like Western abstract art they're not really abstract at all but diagrams with specific meanings. They're usually rather intricate and geometric, with motifs repeated and with a central point on which worshippers can focus for meditation. In *puja*, a *yantra* is worshipped in the same way as any more obvious image. The *sadhaka* meditates upon a god, arouses the god within himself and then communicates the divine presence to the *yantra* which he then worships.

Practical assignment: Meditating on a yantra

The funny thing about *yantras* is that even as Westerners with no knowledge of Tantra we can look at them and somehow feel that they're 'right'. On some level, they still speak to us. You can find examples of *yantras* in books on tantric art.

In Chapter 07 we already looked at various different ways of meditating. Now here's another one. Place your *yantra* where you can easily see it. Begin by taking in the whole design. Just let your eyes roam back and forth, taking in the various elements. Gradually let your focus be drawn in to the centre where there will be a small circle or dot or *yoni* symbol. Concentrate on that. Don't stare and don't glaze over; just look. Don't fight thoughts that come and go but always bring your attention back to the centre afterwards. Close your eyes and try to 'see' the image. One benefit of the exercise is learning to focus on just one thing for a long time. Gradually lengthen the sessions.

Mantra

The chanting of *mantras*, which we encountered in Chapters 05 and 06, is a well-known part of various Eastern religions as well as Tantra. A *mantra* isn't a prayer because the meaning of a prayer is entirely in the words whereas the 'meaning' of a mantra, while it may be partially in the word or words, is also in the sound. Essentially, according to this belief, the whole of the universe is a sound or a series of sounds, or, you could say, vibrations.

It isn't enough merely to mutter a *mantra* or to speak it without knowledge. *Mantras* have to be intoned in the proper way, according to *svara* (rhythm) and *varna* (intonation). They are then extremely powerful because they, as it were, resonate with the divine vibration of the cosmos. You could see it as a way of bringing the body of the worshipper into 'tune' with the universe. Special breathing techniques are another way of creating the vibrations. *Om* is the most powerful and well-known *mantra* but whole sentences are also possible. Endless repetition is *japa* and may be used in meditation. *Mantra* is so important that there are *sadhakas* who concentrate on almost nothing else.

Practical assignment: *Mantras* during sex

As I've already pointed out, you can't just say 'Om' and expect something special to happen. You have to be taught by a guru. But you can very easily learn how to use sound vibrations in sex. We're not really talking about *mantras* here in the proper sense but this practical assignment will give you a feel for the potential of sound vibrations as well as creating some interesting sensations. The idea is to put your mouth on some particularly sensitive part of your partner's body and then intone your mantra. Any short word ending in 'M' works well. Or you could just, sort of, hum with your lips slightly apart and pressed lightly on your partner's skin. The entire vulva, clitoris and penis are obviously pretty good places to try this out. Your aim is to make the flesh vibrate – just in the same way, in fact, that a vibrator would.

Tantra-yoga

Stones seals excavated in the Indus valley and thought to date from around 3000 BCE or even earlier show figures in yogic postures. And if confirmation were needed, the Rig Veda, based on oral traditions that goes back at least as far, also describes yoga. So yoga is probably even older than Tantra.

Yoga was not, as many suppose in the West, a system of exercise especially for flexibility, but a whole philosophy of subjugation of the body through things like *asanas* (postures), regulation of the breath, restraint of the senses, meditation for steadying the mind, and austerities such as no sex. On the face of it, that's the complete opposite Tantra, which identifies sexual energy with cosmic energy. Nevertheless, you can see how with a little adjustment here and there the two things could get together.

Yogis believe that the Absolute, the supreme Brahman, is the inner self, a truth which can only be realised when the mind turns inwards while the body turns off. Tantrikas believe more or less the same, but think the truth can best be apprehended during the altered consciousness of joy, with the body very much turned on. So they seem to be in conflict, and yet it wouldn't have taken a lot of imagination to see how some of the *asanas* could have been adapted for sex – and then you have the best of both approaches.

Maithuna

Maithuna means sex. And, of course, everybody knows that 'traditional Tantra' is really just an excuse for lots of it, especially orgies and free love. Well, not so fast.

In our Western tradition, sex is an animal thing and only acceptable to Western religions when used for procreation. Subsequently, we have a problem viewing it any other way. But, as we've already seen, in Hindu belief sex for pleasure (*kama*) is one of the three sacred essentials for proper living. Tantra added a third role for sex. In Tantra, sex could actually be used as a way of channelling the divine energy.

Traditional Tantra and sex

So, in other words, sex or *maithuna* is just another technique like *mantra, yantra* and so on and, like them, it could be used in different ways. Not everybody chants the same *mantras* and not everybody has the same kind of sex.

Tantra is often divided into 'right-handed' and 'left-handed' forms:

- Right-handed: the mainstream in which the ritual use of taboos was largely symbolic. If real sex took place, a man would make love with his own wife (*Adya Shakti*).
- Left-handed: considered by many Hindus to be a form of 'black magic'. A man might have sex with a woman who was not his wife (*Svakiya Shakti*).

In practice, there never was a sharp division. There were *sadhakas* who never took part in sex rituals at all, there were those who sometimes took part in 'right-handed' sex ceremonies and sometimes in 'left-handed', and there were those who followed the 'left-handed' path exclusively.

Let's take a look, first of all, at *maithuna* in its most extreme form.

Tantra as black magic

One of the more notorious 'black magic' practices was *cudacakra* in which women put their jackets (*cuda*) in a pile and the men then selected one. In another rite known as *anandabhuvana-yoga* a *vira* (a word usually translated as a follower who has achieved 'heroic status') would have sex with anything from three to 108 women. Some commentators say that all but one of the women would merely be touched but, as we know, using the techniques to prevent ejaculation described in Chapters 05 and 08, it would have been possible to have intercourse with a large number of women. It may have happened.

Perhaps the most infamous of the 'black magic' rituals was sex at a cremation ground and those were not nice tidy places like a modern crematorium. There would have been bones and bits of unburned body lying around and scavenged upon by wild animals. At night they would have been terrifying places. The following supplication gives a flavour of the kind of thing that went on:

> O Goddess Kali, he who on a Tuesday midnight having uttered your mantra, makes an offering to you in the cremation ground just once of a [pubic] hair from his female partner pulled out by the root, wet with semen poured from his penis into her menstruating vagina, becomes a great poet, a Lord of the World, and always travels on elephant-back.

As horrifying and disgusting as it sounds there was a logic to it all.

The point is that there's an enormous difference between believing something you've been taught and actually experiencing it for yourself. This kind of tantric sex was all about trying to have that experience. We all know, for example, that we must die. And yet we don't *really* know it. That's to say, we don't live our lives as we logically should. We don't, if Hindus, always live like people who will be reincarnated in accordance with our conduct in this life. We don't, if Christians, always turn the other cheek or accept that the wealthy can't go to Heaven.

The seers of Tantrism reasoned that it needed something as extreme and dramatic as sex at a cremation ground to truly confront the reality of death. They certainly must have succeeded in that.

The secret ritual of the *Pancatattva*

The *Pancatattva* was the 'secret ritual' that, in its different forms, was part of both 'right-handed' and 'left-handed' Tantra. So it could have been 'black magic' or it could have been something more benign. It usually took the form of men and women sitting alternately in a circle, when it was known as *cakrapuja* (*cakra* means circle, *puja* means worship). In the centre sat the Lord of the *cakra* with his Shakti or goddess. Participants would eat the forbidden foods, drink wine and possibly something else containing the semen of the Lord of the *cakra* and then – sometimes high on drugs such as cannabis – have sex.

Put like that it *does* sound like an orgy. And that's exactly how the opponents of Tantra liked to put it. But, most of the time, the way *cakrapuja* was conducted made it something very different. You didn't drink to get drunk, it was more akin to Communion. And you didn't stuff yourself on thick, juicy steak, instead you'd just nibble. And you didn't throw yourself on the woman or man you most fancied in wild abandon. Except in the most extreme versions you had sex with your own wife or husband in a very specific, controlled and even cold manner. Everything was preceded by the most elaborate and lengthy ceremonies which had to be carried out precisely and in the prescribed way. For example, before you could have sex, you'd have to perform *nyasa,* which involved touching many different parts of the body and identifying them, through *mantras*, with the body of the god or goddess. For each part of the body you'd first recite a mantra:

Ang, Kring, Kring, Yang, Rang, Lang, Vang, Shang, Shang, Sang, Hong, Haung, Hangsah.

And then follow that by saying something like, 'The embodied spirit of the highly blessed and auspicious Kalika is placed here.'

That could take so long that, by the end of it, if you'd really only joined for group sex, you'd probably gone off the whole idea. Only if you were a believer would the convoluted rituals mean anything.

So was traditional tantric sex ever enjoyable?

Some commentators argue that, far from being an orgy, the *cakrapuja* was quite deliberately a very dull affair. They point out that it's quite possible, for example, to bring about an erection by manually massaging blood into the penis and that it's quite possible to have intercourse without ever getting anywhere near an orgasm. But that ignores the fundamental point that the whole idea was to channel sexual energy. If there was no sexual energy then nothing could happen. Indeed, the hope was to experience bliss as a taste of the state of continual bliss that awaited those who could break free from the cycle of death and rebirth. The sexual state achieved through Tantra was known as *rasa* (which is often translated as 'juice-joy') or *maharaga* (the great emotion). So, yes, of course traditional tantric sex was enjoyable.

In the Hindu form, ejaculation was sometimes permitted as a kind of sacrifice. In the Buddhist form, ejaculation wasn't permitted at all but, as we've seen in this book, the non-ejaculatory orgasm can take a man far higher than a normal ejaculation.

Nyasa and all the other ceremonies that preceded intercourse would have been, in effect, the world's longest foreplay. Traditional tantric sex would have been mind-blowing.

Practical assignment: *Nyasa* and foreplay

As I've already stressed, you can't follow traditional Tantra without a guru any more than you can proclaim yourself a Catholic by reading a book. But there's no reason you can't incorporate some of the ideas into your Western-style tantric sex. On one level you can regard *nyasa* and all the other rituals as ways of building tension and excitement.

As you undress one another don't rush at it but proceed one garment at a time. Spend a few minutes on each part of the body as it's revealed. Stroke, kiss and suck the skin. Apply perfumed oil. If it appeals to you, you could intone the *mantra* given above. For each part you could then say something appropriate, in accordance with your own feelings. You could say, for example: 'This is the nipple that I'm going to suck and bite until it becomes hard.' If you do believe in the idea of the Divine Consciousness in everyone then you could say something more 'Tantra' such as: 'This vagina/penis is the vagina/penis of the goddess/god with whom I, as a god/goddess, am going to unite.' Whatever you do, take plenty of time before you get to intercourse.

Tantric sex versus Western science

Probably no insight into the nature of the universe is so impressive as the perception in Tantra (and some other Eastern beliefs and religions) that the universe is essentially composed of nothing more (or less) than vibrations. Indeed, western science has confirmed that at the atomic level matter appears as particles or waves. Hence the importance of *mantras*. We now know that at the subatomic level, a particle can also be a wave or a sort of vibration, if you like. Which effectively means that you and I aren't solid as we thought.

At school you may have been taught that everything was composed of tiny atoms. A teacher did a drawing on a blackboard of a large circle representing the hard exterior of the atom with a small solid circle in the middle, representing the nucleus. But, in fact, the 'exterior' of an atom isn't something hard at all, think of it more like a cloud, and the 'interior' is mostly space. In fact, if an atom were to be magnified to the size of the dome of St Paul's Cathedral in London, the nucleus would still only be the size of a grain of salt. The other subatomic particles would be like a few specks of dust whirling around and the rest would be space. Thus a human being is mostly empty space. You are mostly empty space. And, as empty space, it's really just an artificial construction to see yourself as something separate from your partner and from the rest of the mostly empty space that is the universe. *Maya* is at work. If that wasn't already amazing enough, reflect on this. The atoms of which you at this very moment are composed will have been part of several stars and literally millions of Earthly organisms before becoming part of you. In all probability, some of the atoms of which you are at this moment composed previously made up Confucius, Buddha, the various seers who wrote down the Vedas, and any other historical figure you care to mention. I say 'at this moment' because your atoms are constantly being recycled. Today, you are not the same person you were last month. In which case, who or what is the *real* you?

This constant change is all part of Tantra's 'cosmic dance' of Shiva, with everything in continual motion. In fact, as you're reading this, cosmic rays are passing right through you. Fortunately, you won't feel a thing and this process of constant creation and destruction even applies to the entire universe itself. One day, Hindus believe, it will contract to a dot, only to begin all over again with another 'Big Bang'. They believe this cycle will repeat itself again and again. Some modern scientists agree, and some disagree.

These are mind-boggling concepts and in case you're wondering what they've got to do with sex I'll tell you. These Tantric mystics didn't have microscopes and telescopes and all the rest of the scientific instruments we have today. So how did they work these things out? According to the *Upanishads*, the Hindu spiritual treatises, the reality of the universe can only be grasped during a state of consciousness that is different to normal consciousness, a consciousness of joy. In other words, during sex. Now I can't prove they intuited these ideas during lengthy tantric sex sessions but I like to think so. It's during those moments of radiant ecstasy that we can apprehend things beyond the capabilities of our normal senses. As the followers of Tantra say: 'Spirit can alone know Spirit.'

In fact, wherever you look and in whatever age, there were people who believed it was necessary to enter an altered state of consciousness to be able to understand the world. The shamans, the whirling dervishes, the 'witch doctors' and all the rest, they intuited things about the nature of the universe that, through technology, we now know to be true.

So there we are. It was maybe a few thousand years ago in a place we now call India that a man having sex with his wife discovered the secret of the universe. So who knows what you might discover?

How Tantra came to the West

Tantric sex didn't arrive in the West only recently. Incredible as it may seem, during the Victorian era a group of people was practising a kind of tantric sex and 'free love' in a commune in New York. This was the Oneida Community which was founded in 1848. They called their sexual arrangements *Complex Marriage* and the technique they used was called *Male Continence*. In other words, the men *didn't ejaculate*. This wasn't specifically for spiritual reasons so much as practical reasons. Each woman had an average of three partners a week and, in an age before efficient birth control, male continence was a way of trying to prevent the women from all becoming pregnant. It also, of course, allowed the men to have almost unlimited sexual encounters.

However there were others for whom the spiritual aspect of 'male continence' was all important. One of those was a gynaecologist from Chicago called Alice Bunker-Stockham who, having travelled to India, saw that Tantra could have benefits for Westerners. She didn't accept Tantra entirely but invented her own version which she called Karezza after the Italian word *carezza*, meaning 'caress'. It's a fairly apt title because, during intercourse, she recommended couples do just that, and little more. Stockham said she experienced powerful spiritual feelings using this method. Karezza isn't tantric sex but the parallels are obvious.

Practical assignment: Karezza

Prior to sex, prepare yourselves mentally by listening to some beautiful music or reading poetry. Begin sex according to your inclinations but after penetration you should both almost stop moving. You can kiss and cuddle and stroke but with only the occasional thrust to maintain erection. It helps if you haven't had sex for a while, otherwise you may not feel enough excitement. The man can neither orgasm nor ejaculate and in 'advanced' karezza the woman doesn't either. Continue like this for at least an hour. According to Stockham, that was the amount of time necessary for the altered state of consciousness to take over.

Britain's answer to Alice Stockham was Marie Stopes who started the birth control clinics that continue to this day and who wrote a beautiful book called *Married Love*, first published in 1918. Stopes contribution to Western Tantra was her opposition to *coitus interruptus* (in which a man withdraws just before climax and ejaculates outside the vagina) because it prevented a woman absorbing a man's 'secretions'. In her book she wrote that a man shouldn't ejaculate frequently because 'all the vital energy and nerve force' as well as the 'precious chemical substances' could then be retained for other 'creative' things. This, of course, accords with Tantra, particularly the Buddhist school.

Meanwhile, a man who went under the mystical name of Arthur Avalon was intent on promoting not a Westernized version of Tantra but *real* Indian Tantra. He was probably the first Western scholar of Tantra, especially Shakta Tantra which worshipped the 'Supreme Deity' as female. He wrote several books on the subject of which the most famous is *The Serpent Power* (see Chapter 12, Taking it further). In fact, he did somewhat play down the sexual aspects of Tantra but that's hardly surprising given that his real name was Sir John Woodroffe and that he became Advocate General of Bengal and, in 1915, Chief Justice of the High Court of India at Calcutta. Or, rather, he didn't so much play it down as bury it under an avalanche of scholarship which made his books extremely difficult to read. Although he was extremely prolific his books didn't, therefore, have much impact outside intellectual circles.

Probably the first person to get through to large numbers of people in the West was an Indian guru in a beanie who went under the name Bhagwan Shree Rajneesh and later Osho. During the 1960s he made a series of speeches promoting Tantra which the Western press vilified as advocating 'free love'. Which, in fact, he did. His speeches were later compiled under the title *From Sex to Superconsciousness*. Rajneesh said that: 'For Tantra everything is holy, nothing is unholy.' Sex, he argued, had to be thoroughly experienced if it was to be transcended. In fact, Tantra was only one of the many belief systems that he drew on, but it's the one for which he's remembered – along with the various scandals that rocked the community he set up in Wasco County, Oregon in 1981 (including a 'salmonella attack' on local restaurants and a plot to assassinate the U.S. Attorney for Oregon).

Because of those scandals, Tantrikas don't tend to mention Rajneesh much these days. It may also have been because of him that Westerners interested in Tantra set off in a new direction. Among those were Dr Jonn Mumford (Swami Anandakapila Saraswati) whose lectures on Tantra in the USA in 1976 helped shape neo-tantra. At that time male multiple orgasm and female ejaculation weren't the vital aspects of neo-tantra that they've become today. His view was that the G-spot was a trigger point for the Swadisthana Chakra and nothing more. But others did develop these techniques, like Margot Anand whose *The Art of Sexual Ecstasy* brought Tantra to a wide audience in the early 1990s. She still gives courses today. Others who taught this wide range of techniques in the context of couples were Charles and Caroline Muir, whose school of Tantra, once based in Atlanta, is now in Hawaii.

Traditional versus neo-tantra: which is best?

When it comes to sex and your sex life, there's no doubt that the Westernized version of tantric sex is the way it is because it suits Western culture. It's ironic, in fact, that in the West many people (but certainly not all) have now developed the kind of outlook for which we used to look to the East. In a sense, the West has surpassed the East. There's little point in travelling to India to be initiated into the 'mysteries' of sex, the answers are to be found right here. It's here in the West that we have the knowledge of the clitoris and the G-spot and female ejaculation and the prostate gland and all the rest of it. For many couples, nothing is taboo. It's here in the West that we have vibrators and dildos and inflatable sex cushions and aphrodisiacs that really work. And it's here in the West that we have (many of us) as positive an attitude towards sex as has ever existed in the human race. Sex, for us, even sacred sex, is not something we can only practise under the guidance of a guru on certain special occasions. We can have sex, and make it a special 'sacred' occasion, any day we choose and bring to it a wide range of techniques.

Practical assignment: Putting it all together

Not many people in the West or East today would want to follow the traditional tantric sex practices. How far you're willing to is entirely a matter for you. Here are some suggestions for putting together everything we've learned to create as 'traditional' a tantric sex session as possible whilst remaining within the context of a loving relationship.

- Prepare yourselves mentally by contemplating sex purely as a ritual for spiritual purposes.
- If you have a suitable erotic video or DVD put it on so you can be part of a bigger experience.
- Perform *nyasa*, as described earlier. That's to say:
  - Worship one another.
  - Worship one another's sex organs, which should be fully displayed.
  - Begin intercourse with a minimum of bodily contact.
  - Bearing in mind that the *sadhaka* is attached to nothing, hates nothing and is ashamed of nothing, use every kind of sexual technique.
  - Men should use the methods described in Chapters 05 and 08 to prevent orgasm and ejaculation.
  - Don't give any thought to your partner's pleasure but only to maintaining an altered state of consciousness through sex (your partner should do the same).
  - Reflect on the idea that what you think of as 'you' is nothing more than atoms that are constantly exchanged with all the other atoms of the universe.
  - Continue for as long as you can – aim for at least 20 minutes of intercourse, preferably far more.
  - Seek union with the Divine Consciousness, Brahma, God or whatever name you prefer to use.

Summary

In this chapter we have explored how Western style tantric sex (the subject of this book) is quite different to 'traditional' tantric sex in that it is largely concerned with pleasure while 'traditional' tantric sex is only concerned with enlightenment. Traditional tantric sex brings about an altered state of consciousness in which amazing insights are possible. Traditional tantra requires a guru, *puja* and the use of *yantras* and *mantras*; sex (*maithuna*) was only sometimes used.

We have learnt how the origins of Tantra are ancient but the oldest surviving texts date from the seventh century CE.

We have understood how India's tantric rituals were modified under Muslim rule and again under British rule and have also learnt how 'left-handed' Tantra is regarded as 'black-magic' by many Hindus.

Finally, we have explored the introduction of tantric sex to the West since at least the middle of the 19th century and learnt that we are able to choose traditional elements of tantric sex to add to our Western tantric practices in accordance with our own beliefs and desires.

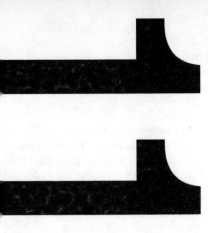

tantric sex toys

In this chapter you will learn:
- how toys can harmonize with tantric sex
- which toys to choose
- how to use sex toys the tantric way.

In the opinion of Babhravya, these Apadravyas [dildos] should be made of gold, silver, copper, iron, ivory, buffalo's horn, various kinds of wood, tin, or lead, and should be soft, cool, provocative of sexual vigour, and well fitted to serve the intended purpose.

The Kama Sutra

Having written so much about the sacredness of sex and the beauty of tantric sex it might seem surprising to write about sex toys. Aren't they just part of a sleazy sexual underground, sold in tacky shops hidden in alleyways? Aren't they just for sad and lonely people to use on their own?

Well, no they're not. Not any more, anyway. Sex toys are nowadays sold in a variety of outlets and endorsed by all kinds of highly esteemed organizations that help sort out relationship and sexual problems. So, sex toys are perfectly respectable. However, there may not seem to be anything very uplifting about a mass-produced orange plastic tube that buzzes like a fly. Tacky is more the word that springs to mind. Well, yes, but things have changed. Artists have got into the business and produced things of elegance and beauty much more suited to the kind of effect that tantric sex is trying to achieve.

Would the original Tantrikas have used this kind of thing? Absolutely. A Vira, that's to say a guru of 'heroic status' might have had 'sex' with up to 108 women in a single session and to do that he would have had to employ a dildo with some of them, or as the *Kama Sutra* called it, an *apadravya*. So these kinds of devices go almost as far back as the invention of sex.

Practical assignment: The sex shop

To see a good selection of sex toys you need to go to a sex shop. Try to go together as a couple. It's a good way of overcoming embarrassment and opening up discussion about the subject. You'll probably see things you'd like to buy but don't feel quite ready to admit to. That's ok, you can always come back another time. There's no hurry. But make up your minds that, whatever happens, you will buy *something*. Some women like to go as a group and have a good laugh but, be warned, you'll need a lot of courage to buy anything in front of your friends.

If there's no convenient sex shop or you're too embarrassed to go in then take a look at the Internet shopping suggestions in Chapter 12.

Vibrators

The most popular sex toy is the vibrator and they do things that human beings just can't manage. Once you've been on the end of one, especially if you're a woman, you'll never want to exclude them from your sexual repertoire. A man can rub his finger backwards and forwards on his partner's clitoris several times a second but that's nowhere near as fast as a vibrator. Quite apart from which, it's just not something a man can keep up for very long whereas a vibrator can continue indefinitely. A vibrator, then, is an essential piece of equipment for any woman who doesn't orgasm easily.

The most popular vibrator models are designed to look like a *lingam*. Some are extremely realistic while others merely approximate the general shape and size. Inside there's a little motor, powered by batteries, that sets up a vibration. Although it's quite different to the kind of stimulation provided by 'normal' sex it's nevertheless highly effective. Some vibrators are made of a fairly soft plastic, which seems less intimidating, but the hard plastic models transmit the vibrations better. To be frank, quite a lot of them *do* look rather tacky which is where the new glass models come in (see page 154).

It's easy to see what the woman can get out of a vibrator but what about the man? Well, for a start, the tantric style of sex is all about sharing joy. If the woman is happy the man should be happy too. But, as we'll see, there are some direct benefits for a man.

How do you use it? At first, most men will probably want to take charge of the vibrator. Well, that's just how men are. If it's anything mechanical they simply assume that only they will be able to understand it. But, in reality, it's much better if the woman uses it on herself. For a start, although most vibrators are designed to look like penises they're not at their best when they're thrust in and out of the vagina. They're far more effective when they're held still on or beside the clitoris, depending on sensitivity. That's why it's best to leave a woman to do it to herself, because only she knows exactly the optimum part of her anatomy to hold it against. While that's going on a man can be simply watching, which is already quite good fun, or he could be holding his lover in his arms and feeling her orgasm. Or he could be inside her in which case he might feel the vibrations as well. Alternatively, he could be using his own vibrator. Held against the shaft of the penis or the glans a vibrator can induce some very enjoyable sensations in a man. Or it can be stroked against the perineum and anal area.

Practical assignment: Exploring vibrators

Make sure that the packaging on your vibrator hasn't been disturbed. Unwrap it and, if it's the plastic battery-powered kind, wash it with soap and water, taking care that no water gets into the battery compartment. Wash again after each use. If it's a mains-powered model follow the hygiene instructions that come with it.

For a man on a woman

The first rule is *communication*. Keep checking with your partner how she's feeling and whether she wants more pressure or less pressure and so on.

Although the vibrator is probably shaped like a penis, don't immediately begin thrusting it in and out. Take time to explore your partner's body and let her experience the new sensations it can create. First of all, raise the level of excitement a little by using the vibrator near her clitoris. If your partner is very sensitive in this area begin on a slow speed and apply it against her underwear. Gradually increase the intensity by turning up the speed, applying to bare skin and moving in steps closer and closer to the clitoris. Don't constantly move the vibrator around; rather move it $1/4$" or $1/2$ cm at a time and hold it in the new position for a while.

Once you've woken her body up try the vibrator in different places. Circle her breasts with it, then her areolae, then her nipples. A vibrator can also do interesting things in the small of the neck and on the feet.

Now put some lubricant on the vibrator and on the entrance to her vagina. This is very important. Gently introduce the vibrator a couple of inches (five centimetres). As she relaxes into the sensations so you can slide it a little further. Remember that a *yoni* is only as long as a finger so, whatever you do, don't attempt to thrust the whole length of the vibrator into her, that will only cause pain. Now try sliding the vibrator backwards and forwards with short movements. In all probability she won't find this particularly enjoyable but she may and it's all part of experimenting to see what feels good. Also try pressing the vibrator against her G-spot – in other words, apply a little pressure in the direction of her pubic mound. Some vibrators are curved to make this easier to do. Finally, return to her vulva and gently hold the vibrator as close as she wants to her clitoris and keep it there, quite still, until she has an orgasm.

For a woman on herself

In truth, it's usually better for a woman to use a vibrator on herself. She knows exactly what feels good and what doesn't and can handle the vibrator with precision.

When you're on your own the inclination is to go straight for the clitoris, but it's worth taking the time to explore the effect of the vibrator all over your body. Try the same things that I've suggested a man does.

Quite a lot of women instinctively react against putting anything unusual into their vaginas. If that includes you, try to overcome your resistance and explore the sensations the vibrator can create there. Use plenty of lubrication. You might enjoy having the vibrator in your vagina while at the same time stimulating your clitoris with your fingers. (And there are vibrators designed to stimulate the vagina and the clitoris simultaneously.) Also apply pressure so the vibrator works on the G-spot. But in all probability you'll find you want to hold the vibrator on or close to your clitoris, which is the surest way for most women to orgasm.

For a woman on a man

When you're making love with your partner and using a vibrator on yourself, there's no reason you shouldn't also use it on him. Try it on his nipples and on different places on the shaft of his penis as well as the glans.

For a man on himself

Try holding the vibrator against different places on your penis. You'll find it can bring you to orgasm. You could also buy an artificial vagina which has been designed more precisely for male pleasure.

During intercourse

During intercourse, try holding the vibrator against the base of the penis. That way, both of you should feel the sensations. When a woman is laying face down on the bed, another good way of using a vibrator is to slide it underneath against the vulva.

Glass dildos and vibrators

In the last few years we've seen the appearance of glass dildos (false *lingams* but without the vibrations) in all kinds of beautiful shapes, often with strands of different colours embedded within them. Some of them are so elegant they actually look like pieces of art. If one of your children or your grandmother spots yours you can always explain it away as a bedside sculpture.

Why would anybody want a dildo, a Kama Sutra style *apadravya*, when modern technology has improved the concept with a motor? The answer is that a lot of these dildos are designed specifically for the G-spot. Just to recap, the G-spot is that slighter rougher area on the roof of the vagina just inside the entrance. A good dildo is designed to hit it every time and, in fact, it's not necessary to have vibrations for the G-spot because it seems to respond best to simple pressure. Choose a design with a chunky rounded head for the most effective stimulation. Certainly a dildo can be thrust in and out but the most effective thing is to insert it and then use the PC muscle to squeeze it against the G-spot. However if you do want vibrations, you can either set your dildo alive by touching a conventional vibrator to the base or, in some cases, buy a special vibrating device that fits into a hole in the dildo.

Apart from the fact that glass dildos look and feel so much nicer than plastic ones they have the advantage of being unbreakable. Well, almost. In fact, they're usually made from pyrex which means you can even put them in the dishwasher. (That may take some explaining if your dinner guests insist on loading the dishwasher for you!) Pyrex has some other advantages over plastic. You can stand your dildo in warm water so it matches your body temperature or, for a completely different sensation, you can put it in the fridge for a while. Another point about glass is that, being so smooth, it doesn't need any artificial lubricant. Or, at any rate, very little.

Specialist vibrators

Humans being the incredibly inventive creatures that they are, it shouldn't come as any surprise that the basic vibrator has been improved in all sorts of ways. Fortunately, they're not very expensive so, over a period of time, you can experiment with different designs:

- **Mains powered models**. Any woman who really has difficulty achieving orgasm, even with a battery-powered vibrator, should consider a mains-powered model. There are two basic sorts. One style doubles as a massager, a very nice idea because it means you can both use it all over your bodies. The other is more specifically designed for use on the clitoris and inside the vagina. Women who orgasm easily should use these very powerful models with caution because they can quickly take you beyond pleasure into a state of numbness.

- **Clitoral vibrators**. Women like plenty of clitoral stimulation so the designers have come up with two different solutions. One is to add some sort of vibrating nub to a conventional vibrator. The most famous is the 'rabbit' whose latex ears tickle the clitoris while the main barrel is inside the vagina. The other style does away with vaginal stimulation altogether and just concentrates on the vulva. Some of these look like showerheads with a stippled pad to arouse the inner labia as well as the clitoris.

- **Fingertip vibrators**. These slip onto a finger so wherever you touch your partner you create an electrifying effect.

- **Nipple vibrators**. If you're easily aroused by nipple stimulation these vibrating clamps will excite you very quickly; if not, man or woman, they can 'teach' your nipples to become more responsive.

- **Novelty vibrators**. There are remote-controlled vibrators, vibrators that respond when your mobile rings, vibrators built into inflatable cushions that you use like space hoppers, vibrators that keep time to music... If you've thought of it, somebody has probably made it.

Specifically for men

It's a fact that most sex toys are designed for women but there are two kinds of sex toys for men that are particularly useful for tantric sex. A third kind, for stimulating the prostate gland, is dealt with below under Anal toys.

Vibrating cock rings

If you have a problem maintaining an erection throughout lengthy tantric sex sessions a vibrating cock ring could be the answer. The old-fashioned cock rings that were designed to keep the *lingam* hard by constricting the outward flow of blood risked doing damage. This new generation of rings don't constrict the penis but work by maintaining constant stimulation.

The first were cumbersome affairs with wires leading to a battery pack but the latest designs are extremely light, don't have wires and are powered by built-in watch batteries.

Of course, it's not just the man who feels the pleasure. There's usually a little raised nub to work on the clitoris and, at the same time, the vibrations are transmitted along the penis and can therefore be felt inside the vagina.

Vibrating yonis

These are designed for men to use on their own or, perhaps, whilst their partners are masturbating with a vibrator. Because of the very realistic feel and intense stimulation they make an excellent training device for practising the lock and all the other techniques for controlling ejaculation that we learned earlier.

Anal toys

Even if you've overcome any reservations about standard vibrators you may still have doubts about anal sex and anal toys. To many people the whole subject sounds 'dirty' in every sense. But, in tantric sex, everything is holy, including the anus.

It's better to buy a second vibrator specifically designed for the purpose rather than use your standard vibrator. Once again, you don't have to buy something plastic if you don't want, you can buy anal toys in glass and even jade. Anal vibrators are narrower and shorter than standard models and usually have a wide base to stop them accidentally slipping all the way in. Apart from that, it's more hygienic to have a separate vibrator for the anal area. There's also a very special kind of anal dildo specifically designed for the prostate gland. After insertion into the rectum via the anus the man flexes his PC muscle to press the head of the dildo against the gland and massage it. As a result, the gland produces an increased quantity of prostatic fluid, leading to longer and more satisfying ejaculations. This is something a man can do whilst masturbating or just prior to beginning a tantric sex session.

Practical assignment: Using anal vibrators

If you're a bit apprehensive about anal penetration, the key is not to go in very deeply – no more than about 2" or 5 cm.

Using an anal vibrator alone

If you've never tried anal stimulation before then the whole idea may take some getting used to. Get yourself a little excited in your usual way before exploring this new area. Then try circling your anus with a lubricated finger. It should feel very nice because the anus is absolutely packed with nerve endings in both men and women. Next try inserting your finger a short way – say as far as the first joint. (Make sure your finger nail is well trimmed.) Once you and the muscle both feel fairly relaxed, apply plenty of lubricant to the vibrator, switch it on and insert it a short distance. As you get used to the sensations so you can ease it further inside if you want or you can just keep it at the entrance where most of the nerve endings are. At the same time you can masturbate in your usual way, if you wish. If you're a man the vibrations will begin to stimulate your prostate gland and, if you use the vibrator long enough, prostatic fluid will begin to seep from the tip of your penis. If you're a woman an anal vibrator can be a good introduction to anal sex. Some models come with different sleeves so you can start with a narrow one and gradually build up the thickness of the vibrator.

Using an anal vibrator during intercourse

A particularly exciting way of using an anal vibrator is for a man to slip it into his partner's rectum during intercourse. This is easiest in a rear-entry position such as *Manner the Sixth* from the *Perfumed Garden*. Both of you will then be able to feel the vibrations, which can be a mind-blowing experience. During intercourse, apply some lubricant to her anal area and make circling movements with your finger until the muscle relaxes. Apply more lubricant to the vibrator, switch it on and slowly and gently introduce it. Check that your partner is happy. It's a fun idea to keep the vibrator in tandem with your penis. In other words, when your penetration of her vagina is shallow, then keep the vibrator shallow as well. When you go deeper with your penis, move the vibrator a little deeper. She'll feel the vibrations throughout her pubic area and you'll feel them along your penis. It can be intensely exciting for both of you. Remember that the rectum is an extremely delicate area so always be very gentle.

The other way of using an anal vibrator during intercourse is to slip it into the man's rectum. A woman should be able to do this to her partner during a man-on-top position. It's a particularly useful technique for a woman to use if she feels herself approaching orgasm and wants her partner to come at the same time. The first step is to reach around and apply a well-lubricated finger to the anal area; when the muscle is relaxed the woman can then insert the vibrator, also well-lubricated. Alternatively, a man can do this for himself. Most men will ejaculate fairly quickly.

Mirrors

In the context of a loving couple you won't be wanting to make love together with other people (as traditional Tantrikas may do). A mirror can provide a solution, or better still, two mirrors. Most people find it very arousing to see their reflection in a mirror as they have sex.

Practical assignment: Using a mirror

The best place for a mirror is on the wall above the bed angled slightly downwards. If you don't want it to be too obvious what the mirror is for you could attach it by a hinge along the bottom edge of the frame. A length of cord running from the top of the frame to a fixing on the wall can be used for adjustment; the mirror can then be kept flush to the wall when not in use. When you're making love, use the cord to get the right angle and tie it off. If you don't want to go to all that trouble, buy a free-standing full-length mirror and just pull it up close to the bed when you feel like it. Two mirrors facing one another on opposite sides of the bed provide an infinite number of reflections. Then you can feel you're taking part in a traditional tantric *Pancatattva* ceremony with other couples – except that all of them are you.

Swings

Swings feature quite a lot in Indian erotic art but there's no need to buy a special swing from a sex shop. Any swing will do but it's probably better if the seat is fabric rather than wood. Hammock-style swinging seats are ideal but the main problem is where to install it. In the garden is only going to be possible if you have some genuinely secret corner where no neighbours can see. If you want to hang a swing inside then you're going to need some very strong roof beams. Probably best to get a qualified builder to install it otherwise the result may not be quite what you were hoping for. Alternatively look for a model that has its own supporting structure.

Practical assignment: Exploring swings

The idea of the swing is fairly simple. The woman can sit with her legs apart and the man can stand or kneel, depending on the height. All that's then necessary is to nudge the swing backwards and forwards. A woman can do this herself by wrapping her legs around her partner. To make things even more erotic the woman can place her feet on the seat beside her buttocks or even raise her legs up and entwine them round the supporting ropes. With some designs the woman may also be able to lay face down across the swing. Alternatively the man can sit on the swing while the woman adopts a rear-entry position such as The Congress of the Cow from the *Kama Sutra*.

Some Indian erotic paintings show *two* swings where the man and woman face one another with their legs up in the air, pressing the soles of their feet against one another's, in order to gently move the swings back and forth. Not easy!

Final word

This is a book in the *Teach Yourself* series. Please feel free to follow up this wide and varied subject. I recommend some books in the next chapter. Modern translations of all the ancient texts are available; but, be warned, some of them are pretty hard going. There are courses and workshops you can attend if you please – again listed in Chapter 12. Remember, however, that you can only learn by practise; no books or courses are going to teach you anything nearly as well as a considerate, caring, patient lover. You can be their teacher, too. Sex may seem to be a serious subject, but it's not really; sex is about having fun and enjoyment; about opening yourself up to pleasure as the greatest embodiment of human satisfaction; about reunion with the fundamental energy of the universe; about taking part in the richness and excitement of being alive. And it's all free. Having sex is being rich.

Summary

In this chapter we have learnt that sex toys can be employed in tantric sex and were in use at the time of the *Kama Sutra*.

We have also learnt that visiting a sex shop with your partner is a good way of overcoming embarrassment about sex toys.

Vibrators are the most popular sex toys and it's often best for a woman to use a vibrator on herself. They're most effective when placed on or close to the clitoris, depending on sensitivity, and kept still. In addition to the standard *lingam*-shaped vibrator there are all kinds of other designs that can be bought over a period of time.It's not simply vibrators that are particularly suited to tantric sex but also glass dildos.

Other sex toys involve vibrating cock rings which can help a man maintain an erection during lengthy tantric sex sessions and vibrating vaginas which can help a man learn control. Anal sex toys can also add extra excitement.

Finally we have explored how mirrors can simulate the traditional *Pancatattva* ceremony and how swings, often featured in Indian erotic art, can also be used in a tantric way.

taking it further

In this chapter you will learn:
- what to read next
- where to go next for courses and more information
- where to find Tantra on the Internet.

Women have no idea that their bellies contain their whole capacity for ecstasy and wisdom, so they try to flatten them to be more like men. This cuts them off from their sources of pleasure and deadens their genius.

Ma Ananda Sarita and Swami Anand Geho,
Tantric Love

Further reading

Sir John Woodroffe, Tantra and Bengal: An Indian Soul in a European Body?, Kathleen Taylor, Routledge Curzon, 2001

We've already met Sir John Woodroffe. He was the British High Court Judge who played a key role in bringing Tantra to the West. He wrote as the mystical 'Arthur Avalon', a pseudonym which, as he readily admitted, covered not just himself but also various Indian scholars, including his close friend A.B. Ghose. Probably his best-known book was *The Serpent Power* which introduced 'Kundalini Yoga' to the West. This biography is in two parts; the first part focuses on Woodroffe's life in Calcutta at the beginning of the 20th century and the second part is an assessment of his handling of his subject and his contribution to Western understanding of Tantra.

The Serpent Power: Secrets of Tantric and Shaktic Yoga, Arthur Avalon, Dover Publications, 1976

This is the most famous of the books by Sir John Woodroffe, writing under the pseudonym of Arthur Avalon. The serpent is, of course, Kundalini, the energy that Tantrikas believe lies coiled at the base of the spine, and this is the book that did so much to introduce the concept to the West. Most of the book is taken up with Woodroffe's lengthy and learned Introduction which is followed by translations of two Tantras.

Kundalini Yoga: A Brief Study of Sir John Woodroffe's 'The Serpent Power', M.P. Pandit, Motilal Banarsidass, India, 2002

For a critique of *The Serpent Power*, read this assessment by M.P. Pandit.

The Great Liberation, Sir John Woodroffe, Nesma Books, India, 2001

Mahanirvana Tantra of the Great Liberation, Arthur Avalon, R.A. Kessinger Publishing Co., 2004

The *Mahanirvana Tantra* or, to give it its English title, *Tantra of the Great Liberation*, is regarded as Sir John Woodroffe's/ Arthur Avalon's most important translation. The Tantra was first published in Bengali in 1876 and an 'inaccurate version' – according to Woodroffe – appeared in English in Calcutta around the turn of the century. He determined to set the record straight. His real reason for selecting it, however, was probably that it presented a relatively 'safe' version of Tantra, acceptable to intellectual Hindus and the least likely to cause offence in Britain. He admitted as much in his Preface: 'This Tantra is, further, one which is well known and esteemed,' he wrote, 'though perhaps more highly so amongst that portion of the Indian public which favours "reformed" Hinduism than amongst some Tantrikas, to whom, as I have been told, certain of its provisions appear to display unnecessary timidity.' Clearly, Woodroffe wanted to distance himself from those 'Tantrikas' as if he himself had no contact with them. Nevertheless, this is an important chance to read an actual Tantra rather than just a book about Tantra.

The New Art of Sexual Ecstasy, Margot Anand, Harper Collins, 2003
Sexual Ecstasy: The Art of Orgasm, Margot Anand, Tarcher, 2000
The Sexual Ecstasy Workbook: The Path of Skydancing Tantra, Margot Anand and Philip D. Johncock, Tarcher, 2005
Margot Anand's *The Art of Sexual Ecstasy* was one of the seminal books of the neo-tantric movement. *The New Art of Sexual Ecstasy* is the updated version and covers sex as a means of communication between human spirits and includes all the important techniques such as multiple orgasm for men and women. Another two of her books, which are well worth reading, are *Sexual Ecstasy: the Art of Orgasm*, which details techniques for local, whole body and prolonged orgasm, and *The Sexual Ecstasy Workbook*, a brief practical guide.

Spiritual Sex: Secrets of Tantra from Ice Age to the New Millennium, Nik Douglas, Pocket Books, 1998
Sexual Secrets: The Alchemy of Ecstasy, Nik Douglas, Inner Traditions Bear and Co., 1999
Nik Douglas is an authority on Tantra, having spent years travelling in India, Sri Lanka, Nepal, Sikkim, Thailand and Indonesia and studying with such figures as Ajit Mookerjee, Durga Das Shastri, Dudjom Rinpoche and Gangotri Giri. His film *Tantra: Indian Rites of Ecstasy* was produced by Mick Jagger and Robert Fraser and includes footage of a sex ritual and the cremation ground at Tarapith. The first of these two books seeks out the roots of Tantra in prehistoric times and

follows the development of the beliefs and techniques up to the modern era. It's a serious book for those with a genuine interest in the subject. The second title is a best-seller and covers technique in detail.

Ecstasy Through Tantra, Jonn Mumford, Llewellyn, 1988
Dr Jonn Mumford, also known as Swami Anandakapila Saraswati, wrote his first book, *Psychosomatic Yoga*, in 1961 and has been a significant force in the development of Tantra in the West ever since. A man who straddles East and West, he is reputed to be able to slow his heartbeat to almost nothing, hold his breath for over five minutes and stop and start bleeding. This is a book for those who are interested in the "sex magick" aspect of Tantra. His other books include *The Chakra and Kundalini Workbook*, *The Karma Manual* and *Death: Beginning or End?*

An Introduction to Asian Religions, E. G. Parrinder, SPCK, 1958

Anne Hooper's Kama Sutra, Anne Hooper, Dorling Kindersley, 1994

Chakras for Beginners, Naomi Ozaniec, Hodder & Stoughton, 1995

Chinese Horoscopes for Beginners, Kristyna Arcarti, Hodder & Stoughton, 1995

The Clouds and the Rain; the Art of Love in China, Michael Beurdeley, H. Hammond, 1969

Erotic Art of the East, Philip Rawson, Weidenfeld & Nicolson, 1973

Exotic Massage for Lovers, Timothy Freke, Eddison Sadd Edition, 1996

Extended Massive Orgasm, Steve Bodansky and Vera Bodansky, Hunter House Books, 2000

Fundamentals of Human Sexuality, Herant A. Katchadourian and Donald T. Lunde, Holt, Rinehart & Winston, Inc., 1972

The Illustrated Kama Sutra of Vatsyayana, translated by Sir Richard Burton, Fraser Stewart Books, 1992

The Kama Sutra, translated by Sir Richard Burton, Panther Books, 1963

The Mythology of Sex, Sarah Denning, Batsford Books, 1996

The Perfumed Garden of the Shaykh Nefzawi, translated by Sir Richard Burton, Panther Books, 1963

The Pocket Book of Foreplay, Richard Craze, Hunter House Books, 2000

The Pocket Book of Sexual Fantasies, Richard Craze, Hunter House Books, 2000

The Sensual Touch, Dr Glenn Wilson, MacDonald Orbis, 1989

Sex in History, Reay Tannahill, Sphere Books, 1990

Sexual Awareness, Barry and Emily McCarthy, Headline Books, 1991

Sexual Energy Ecstasy, David and Ellen Ramsdale, Bantam Books, 1991

Sexual Pleasure, Barbara Keesling, Hunter House Books, 1993

Simultaneous Orgasm, Michael Riskin and Anita Banker-Riskin, Hunter House Books, 1997

Sky Dancer, Keith Dowman, Routledge & Kegan Paul, 1984

The Spiritual Traditions of Sex, Richard Craze, Godsfield Press, 1996

Tantra: The Art of Conscious Loving, Charles and Caroline Muir, Mercury House, 1989

Tantra: The Key to Sexual Power & Pleasure, Ashley Thirleby, Dell, 1978

Tantra: The Path to Blissful Sex, Leora Lightwoman, Piatkus, 2004

Tantra: The Yoga of Sex, Omar Garrison, Avon Books, 1973

Tantric Love, Ma Ananda Sarita and Swami Anand Geho, Gaia Books, 2001

Tantric Orgasm for Women, Diana Richardson, Inner Traditions Bear and Co., 2004

Tantric Sex, E. J. Gold, Peak Skill Publishing, 1988

Tantric Sex, Cassandra Lorius, Thorsons, 1999

Tantric Sex, Robert Moffett, Berkely Medallion, 1974

The Tantric Way, Ajit Mookerjee and Madhu Khanna, New York Graphic Society, 1977

The Tao of Health, Sex, and Longevity, Daniel Reid, Fireside, 1989

The Tao of Love, Jolan Chang, Wildwood House Ltd, 1977

The Tao of Sex, Akira Ishihira and Howard Levy, Integral Publishing, 1989

Taoist Yoga and Sexual Energy, Eric Steven Yudelove, Llewellyn Publications, 2000

Yoga, Ernest Wood, Penguin Books, 1959

Tantric sex and the Internet

All the following websites have links to others. You can click and surf and find out what is happening in the world of tantra on the Internet. We only include websites that we have personally visited and can recommend. There are, however, a lot more which you can visit yourself to gather what information you need about tantra courses in your own area.

www.tantric.about.com

An excellent starting point with links to well over 100 tantric sites.

www.shivashakti.com/tantric

Helpful information on Tantra as well as other Eastern religions and practices together with a very long list of extremely interesting links.

www.tantra.com

A site that covers everything to do with neo-tantra, including details of all the 'latest' techniques such as male multiple orgasm and female ejaculation. Also an online shop from which you can buy books, music and sex toys.

www.tantraworks.com

A useful site from author Nik Douglas (see earlier) with excellent links and brief articles on a range of Tantra subjects including art, temples, ancient Tantra and modern versions.

www.sacred-texts.com

An excellent website that contains all the great sacred texts of the world. As far as Tantra is concerned, you can read Sir John Woodroffe's translation of the *Mahanirvana Tantra* (see earlier), together with his hugely detailed Introduction, as well as several of his essays on the subject. None of what he wrote is easy going and, writing at the beginning of the 20th century, he was extremely cautious about sex. Nevertheless, anyone who has a serious interest will get more out of this than any more recent works.

http://goddessontheloose.com

Anyaa McAndrew has taken over what used to be the website for Charles and Caroline Muir. If you click on www.tantrainatlanta.com (the old website address) you'll now get transferred to the 'goddess on the loose'. As the title suggests, Anyaa, who trained with the Muirs, is especially interested in empowering women and Tantra is only one of the subjects she teaches. Meanwhile, the Source School of Tantra, which was founded by the Muirs, is to be found at www.sourcetantra.com.

www.sourcetantra.com

Charles and Caroline Muir were among the pioneers of Tantra in America and the Source School of Tantra was founded by them. On this site you'll find a shop, features and book excerpts. Courses are also available (see later).

www.asiatica.org/publications/ijts/

The by-subscription *International Journal of Tantric Studies* online. Very learned articles about the history of Tantra, its diverse forms and its practitioners.

www.tantramagazine.com

Another online magazine, much easier to read than the IJTS and leaning more towards modern Western practice.

www.tootallblondes.com

A very wacky website run by two very tall blonde women – Kate and Barbara – who run a series of workshops and lectures. Visit their site for an updated list of tour dates and venues.

Barbara has combined her experiences in tantra, tao, quodoushka, reiki, rebirthing, metaphysics, performance, ritual, herbal medicine, bodywork and erotic massage into unique and pioneering workshops for women and men. These workshops create a vision of what conscious and sacred sexuality can bring to an individual's personal journey and to the healing of sexual abuse and misuse on the planet.

She has been featured in the videos *Selfloving*, *The Sluts & Goddesses Video Workshop*, *Zen Pussy*, in the film *Sacred Sex*, the HBO television special *Real Sex*, Australian television's *Sex/Life* and on Britain's Sky Channel as part of the documentary *Sex in America*. She collaborated with Annie Sprinkle to present a new/ancient vision of female sexuality in theatrical form in *MetamorphoSex*, a week-long workshop for women culminating in ritual performances. She also directed the Australian premiere of Annie's renowned one-woman show, *Post Porn Modernist*. Barbara's newest performance piece is *Too Tall Blondes in LOVE*, written and performed with her too tall blonde partner, Kate Bornstein.

Barbara was once named the Best Tantric Sex Seminar Leader in New York City by *Time Out Magazine* for her pioneering series of Urban Tantra workshops.

www.Maui.net/~niyaso/

A useful website for courses run by Niyaso Carter and Paul Carter, PhD, in Hawaii. They also run women's retreats, make sacred sex videos, lecture in North America and carry out tantra counselling. In the tantric sex world they are both highly respected and very good teachers. They call their work 'transformational adventures'.

www.greatsex.com

This website doesn't do much in itself but it does transport you to an enormous website – **lightworksav.com** – which is the biggest provider of tantric sex videos and other products.

www.tantra.org/virato.htm

A website run by the US Church of Tantra. This is a very comprehensive site offering products, advice and a history of tantra.

The site is run by Swami Nostradamus who is a sannyasin (follower) of Osho (Bhagwan Shree Rajneeshi) and has been teaching the tantric lifestyle for over 25 years. Articles about him have appeared in the *N.Y. Times*, *Penthouse Magazine*, *Philadelphia Magazine*, *SCAN Magazine*, *New York Magazine* and other publications. He has appeared on numerous national and international television programmes, and was the first to take tantra to Russia in 1992.

This website offers products such as videos, books and audiocassettes as well as a series of intelligent and informative articles on such subjects as *Kama Sutra*, Yoni Massage, Sacred Orgasms, Sex Magic, Basis of Tantra, Lingam Massage, Tantric Yoga, Spiritual Ecstasy, The Tantric Path, Polarity Process Feedback, Fantasy Will in Tantra, Left Hand Path, American Tantra, Lesbian Sex, Breath Control, Karezza, Psychic Protection and Tantra Overview.

It also offers courses and workshops. Log on for details. The membership entitles you to discounts on the products and an eight-week lesson plan. All the articles are available to non-members.

Internet shopping: UK

www.passion8.com

A reliable UK supplier with a wide range of sex toys, lingerie, lubricants and erotica.

www.coco-de-mer-shop.co.uk

The mail-order department of the elegant Covent Garden shop selling luxurious jade dildos, edible massage oils, body jewellery, whips and, in fact, everything for wealthy lovers.

www.sextoys.co.uk

www.bedroompleasures.co.uk

www.lovehoney.co.uk

Internet shopping: USA

http://store.sextoys.sex-superstore.com

www.toyssexshop.com

Workshops and courses

Most workshops in the West teach the style of tantric sex with which this book is mostly concerned. As we've seen, some people call it 'neo-tantra' to distinguish it from the traditional forms but there *are* gurus in the West who lead *cakras* (circles or groups) in the original Oriental style of Tantra. And, of course, the 'Eastern' and 'Western' styles can themselves take various different forms. So the first thing to do is to find out precisely what style of tantric sex is being taught and what you'll be expected to do. Some workshops are 'clothes on' and you'll only practise intimate techniques in the privacy of your own room. At the other extreme are courses where students will, at some stage, explore sacred sex in the company of others or even with different partners. If a course is to be any good it should be taking you further than you've ever been before but be certain before you sign up that it's not taking you too far beyond your present comfort zone or into areas which, for you, could result in the complete opposite of bliss.

Find out something about the credentials of the people leading the course. Ask who they studied with, find out how many courses they've already led and see if you can get any testimonials. After you've spoken to them ask yourself this: 'Do these people sound as if they've reached a higher level?' If you're taking a course close to where you live you may not be risking a lot of money but if you're contemplating flying somewhere for several days the outlay could be significant so you're entitled to ask questions. If the course seems unreasonably expensive and its leaders overly eager to receive your deposit then you may feel they haven't themselves reached the higher state to which you yourself aspire. However, it's not just an issue of money. You could be setting yourself up for psychological and relationship problems if your teachers don't really know what they're doing. If you sign up for 'tantric sex' then sex, in some form or another, is what you're going to get. But in the traditional system, before the power of sex was unleashed, you first had to demonstrate that you had attained a certain emotional and spiritual level. 'Beginners' (*pashus*) weren't allowed to have sex. On many modern tantric sex courses that safeguard doesn't apply and if you're a stable person there's probably no risk but if you're a person with issues from your past a course could unleash unexpected forces. Remember that anybody can set themselves up as an expert on Tantra. Be cautious.

United Kingdom

www.tantralaboratory.com and www.skydancing.org.uk

Courses in sacred sexuality run by John Hawken who trained with Margot Anand. Mostly they're held at the Field of Dreams near Penzance, Cornwall. A course known as The Sacred Couple involves five blocks of five days spread over the course of almost a year. Block 1 is to do with releasing energy and replacing the negative feelings about sex that we learn as children. Blocks 2 and 3 take those processes further. Block 4 covers extended arousal and Block 5 deals with channelling sexual energy into the higher chakras. It's not cheap but there are affordable weekend courses that serve as an introduction.

183 Godstow Road

Oxford

OX2 8PG

Tel: 00 44 (0)1865 428 374

E-mail: tantra@ntlworld.com

www.artofbeing.com

The Art of Being was founded by Alan Lowen in 1986. Tantra is just one aspect of the teaching, whose essence is that 'to be here now is to be in love.' In Britain and Europe the workshops are led by Jan Day who has worked with Alan Lowen for 19 years. She says the themes of 'sexual healing, self-acceptance, forgiveness and loving kindness' are central to her work.

Meru Wray
58 Kingscourt Lane
Rodborough,
Stroud
Gloucestershire,
GL5 3PX
Tel: 00 44 (0)1453 752 604/020 7870 1774
E-mail: uk@artofbeing.com

www.diamondlighttantra.com

Workshops run by Leora Lightwoman, the author of *Tantra: The Path to Blissful Sex* (see above). She is yet another who trained with Margot Anand. Her introductory evenings are a cheap way of finding out whether or not you want to take things further.

Diamond Light Tantra
PO Box 38204
London
NW3 6YZ.
Tel: 00 44 (0)8700 780 584
E-mail: enquiries@diamondlighttantra.com

Tim Broughton

3, St Clements Hill
Norwich
Norfolk
NR3 4DE
Tel: 00 44 (0)1603 788 221
E-mail: tim-broughton@waitrose.com

www.schoolofawakening.com

Tantra training for couples and individuals, meditation CDs and Shiva/Shakti massage oils.

PO Box 15
Chumleigh
Exeter
EX18 7SR
tel: 00 44 (0)1769 581 232
E-mail: webinfo@schoolofawakening.com

www.tantra.uk.com

Transcendence was set up in 1998 by Martin Jelfs. He has been interested in tantra for 20 years and has trained in tantra since 1995. For the last four years he has been in training with Sarita and Geho and has also trained in tantric kriya yoga. Martin is a UKCP Registered Psychotherapist and BACP Senior Registered Counsellor and Supervisor with 18 years' professional experience in personal development. He is a trainer and author of *Manual for Action*.

Shakti Hanna has practised healing meditation, tai chi, chi quong and other ways of working with energy for ten years. She has trained with Bodhi Avinasha, Teja and Ambar in kriya tantra and with Sarita and Geho. She is a holistic architect and reiki and karuna master, running empowerment dance workshops and is currently training in counselling and colourpuncture.

Sahgia
Shaftesbury Road
Compton Chamberlayne
Salisbury
Wiltshire
SP3 5DJ
Tel: 00 44 (0)845 345 8593
E-mail: m.jelfs@zen.co.uk

USA

www.margotanand.com

Margot Anand was one of the great popularizers of tantric sex in the West. She studied with Osho and is an adjunct faculty member at Deepak Chopra's institute and has written several books including *The Art of Sexual Ecstasy*. Her style of teaching is said to be 'a synthesis of French erotic humour, American pragmatism, and Indian mysticism.' She calls it SkyDancing Tantra.

PO Box 2967
San Rafael
California
94912-2967
USA
Tel: 00 1 415 454 6030
E-mail: skyoffice@infoasis.com

www.sourcetantra.com

The Source School of Tantra, which was founded by Western-style tantric sex pioneers Charles and Caroline Muir, offers a variety of courses on the mainland USA and Hawaii. There are weekend courses for beginners, longer courses for advanced students and week-long learning holidays on Hawaii itself. For those who don't want to travel there's a simple home-study course involving DVDs, CDs and a book.

Source School of Tantra

PO Box 368, Kahului,

Hawaii

96733

USA.

Tel: 00 1 888 682 6872

www.ecstaticliving.com

The Institute for Ecstatic Living was set up by Steve and Lokita Carter who studied with Margot Anand. Their workshops include tantric massage and 'timeless loving' and they also run holidays. On their website you can buy DVDs, videos, books and music.

Institute for Ecstatic Living

PO Box 1356

Middletown

California

95461

USA

Tel: Toll Free 877 982 6872

Tel: 00 1 707 987 3456

E-mail: info@ecstaticliving.com

www.artofbeing.com

The Art of Being was founded by Alan Lowen in 1986. Tantra is just one aspect of the teaching, whose essence is that 'to be here now is to be in love.'

The Art of Being

PO Box 790269

Paia

Hawaii

HI 96779

USA

Tel: 00 1 808 572 1435

E-mail: info@artofbeing.com

www.schooloftantra.com

Run by Sasha Lessin and his wife Janet Kira Lessin on Maui, the school has a leaning towards 'polyamory'. That's to say, exploring tantric sex with multiple partners.

1371 Malaihi Road
Wailuku
Maui
Hawaii
96793
USA
Tel: 00 1 808 244 4103
E-mail: schooloftantra@aol.com

Australia

www.tantrananda.com

The Tantrananda School of Tantra was set up by Maria Martins (Bhakti Shakti) in Sydney. It says it follows Kaula Tantra, often referred to as 'left-hand'.

Tel: 00 61 (0)2 9264 6600
E-mail: globlint@ozemail.com.au

Germany

www.art-of-being.de

Saleem Matthias Riek and Gabrielle Nutan Riek
Vaubanallee 43
Freiburg
D 79100
Tel: 00 49 (0)761 453690
E-mail: info@art-of-being.de

www.sinnliche-wege.de

Devaka Hoffman
Heilpraktikerin
Baseler Str. 24
Schallstadt
D79227
Tel: 00 49 (0)761 797966
E-mail: devaka@sinnliche-wege.de

Switzerland

www.kontaktdialog.ch

Stefan Eigenmann
Werkstatt for Contact & Dialog
Bahnhofstrasse 34
CH-Bulach
Tel: 00 41 439 28 300
E-mail: werkstatt@kontaktdialog.ch

India

There are plenty of resources now in the West for learning about tantric sex. But if you want to get back to Tantra's roots and explore the traditional methods then you should consider visiting India. The areas in which Tantra was strongest, and in which it's still practised to a certain degree today, include Bengal, Kashmir, Orissa, Kerala and Madhya Pradesh. There are places you can study Tantra during a holiday but many schools and gurus demand a much more significant commitment. If you're interested, do plenty of research before making a choice. Ask people who've already been to share their experiences with you.

www.indiayogi.com

As the name suggests, this site is more to do with yoga than Tantra but it does have some useful information including details of ashrams (spiritual centres) in India.

www.osho.org and www.meditate-celebrate.com

Osho, also known as Bhagwan Shri Rajneesh (1931–1990) was one of the first to promote neo-tantra (and many other beliefs) in the West. Take note that free love was one of Osho's teachings. Although he was eventually banned from the USA, his organization still has centres in India, of which the most important is the Osho Commune at Pune. If you like, you can just go there as a guest in the same way that you might book into a spa. It's a way of getting a feel for what goes on without committing yourself to anything.

Osho Commune International
17, Koregaon Park
Pune 411 001
Maharashtra
India
Tel: 00 91 20 5601 9999
E-mail: resortinfo@osho.net

www.yogavision.net

One of the most famous in India, the Bihar School of Yoga offers short-term courses in a variety of subjects including Tantra. Located on top of a hill near Munger, the school has lovely views of the Ganges and surrounding area.

P.O. Rikhia

Dist. Deoghar

Jharkhand

814 112

India

Tel: 00 91 64 3223 2870

www.tantra.ifc-the-art-of-conscious-love.com

The IFC Temple of Divine Love teaches all aspects of Tantra.

118/1b Killamkulam Village

Periyur Taluk

Madurai Dist

South India

index

teach yourself®

From Advanced Sudoku to Zulu, you'll find everything you need in the **teach yourself** range, in books, on CD and on DVD.

Visit **www.teachyourself.co.uk** for more details.

Advanced Sudoku and Kakuro
Afrikaans
Alexander Technique
Algebra
Ancient Greek
Applied Psychology
Arabic
Aromatherapy
Art History
Astrology
Astronomy
AutoCAD 2004
AutoCAD 2007
Ayurveda
Baby Massage and Yoga
Baby Signing
Baby Sleep
Bach Flower Remedies
Backgammon
Ballroom Dancing
Basic Accounting
Basic Computer Skills
Basic Mathematics
Beauty
Beekeeping
Beginner's Arabic Script
Beginner's Chinese Script
Beginner's Dutch

Beginner's French
Beginner's German
Beginner's Greek
Beginner's Greek Script
Beginner's Hindi
Beginner's Italian
Beginner's Japanese
Beginner's Japanese Script
Beginner's Latin
Beginner's Mandarin Chinese
Beginner's Portuguese
Beginner's Russian
Beginner's Russian Script
Beginner's Spanish
Beginner's Turkish
Beginner's Urdu Script
Bengali
Better Bridge
Better Chess
Better Driving
Better Handwriting
Biblical Hebrew
Biology
Birdwatching
Blogging
Body Language
Book Keeping
Brazilian Portuguese

Gardening
Genetics
Geology
German
German Conversation
German Grammar
German Phrasebook
German Verbs
German Vocabulary
Globalization
Go
Golf
Good Study Skills
Great Sex
Greek
Greek Conversation
Greek Phrasebook
Growing Your Business
Guitar
Gulf Arabic
Hand Reflexology
Hausa
Herbal Medicine
Hieroglyphics
Hindi
Hindi Conversation
Hinduism
History of Ireland, The
Home PC Maintenance and
  Networking
How to DJ
How to Run a Marathon
How to Win at Casino Games
How to Win at Horse Racing
How to Win at Online Gambling
How to Win at Poker
How to Write a Blockbuster
Human Anatomy & Physiology
Hungarian
Icelandic
Improve Your French
Improve Your German
Improve Your Italian
Improve Your Spanish
Improving Your Employability

Indian Head Massage
Indonesian
Instant French
Instant German
Instant Greek
Instant Italian
Instant Japanese
Instant Portuguese
Instant Russian
Instant Spanish
Internet, The
Irish
Irish Conversation
Irish Grammar
Islam
Italian
Italian Conversation
Italian Grammar
Italian Phrasebook
Italian Starter Kit
Italian Verbs
Italian Vocabulary
Japanese
Japanese Conversation
Java
JavaScript
Jazz
Jewellery Making
Judaism
Jung
Kama Sutra, The
Keeping Aquarium Fish
Keeping Pigs
Keeping Poultry
Keeping a Rabbit
Knitting
Korean
Latin
Latin American Spanish
Latin Dictionary
Latin Grammar
Latvian
Letter Writing Skills
Life at 50: For Men
Life at 50: For Women

Life Coaching
Linguistics
LINUX
Lithuanian
Magic
Mahjong
Malay
Managing Stress
Managing Your Own Career
Mandarin Chinese
Mandarin Chinese Conversation
Marketing
Marx
Massage
Mathematics
Meditation
Middle East Since 1945, The
Modern China
Modern Hebrew
Modern Persian
Mosaics
Music Theory
Mussolini's Italy
Nazi Germany
Negotiating
Nepali
New Testament Greek
NLP
Norwegian
Norwegian Conversation
Old English
One-Day French
One-Day French – the DVD
One-Day German
One-Day Greek
One-Day Italian
One-Day Portuguese
One-Day Spanish
One-Day Spanish – the DVD
Origami
Owning a Cat
Owning a Horse
Panjabi
PC Networking for Small
   Businesses

Personal Safety and Self
   Defence
Philosophy
Philosophy of Mind
Philosophy of Religion
Photography
Photoshop
PHP with MySQL
Physics
Piano
Pilates
Planning Your Wedding
Polish
Polish Conversation
Politics
Portuguese
Portuguese Conversation
Portuguese Grammar
Portuguese Phrasebook
Postmodernism
Pottery
PowerPoint 2003
PR
Project Management
Psychology
Quick Fix French Grammar
Quick Fix German Grammar
Quick Fix Italian Grammar
Quick Fix Spanish Grammar
Quick Fix: Access 2002
Quick Fix: Excel 2000
Quick Fix: Excel 2002
Quick Fix: HTML
Quick Fix: Windows XP
Quick Fix: Word
Quilting
Recruitment
Reflexology
Reiki
Relaxation
Retaining Staff
Romanian
Running Your Own Business
Russian
Russian Conversation

Russian Grammar
Sage Line 50
Sanskrit
Screenwriting
Second World War, The
Serbian
Setting Up a Small Business
Shorthand Pitman 2000
Sikhism
Singing
Slovene
Small Business Accounting
Small Business Health Check
Songwriting
Spanish
Spanish Conversation
Spanish Dictionary
Spanish Grammar
Spanish Phrasebook
Spanish Starter Kit
Spanish Verbs
Spanish Vocabulary
Speaking On Special Occasions
Speed Reading
Stalin's Russia
Stand Up Comedy
Statistics
Stop Smoking
Sudoku
Swahili
Swahili Dictionary
Swedish
Swedish Conversation
Tagalog
Tai Chi
Tantric Sex
Tap Dancing
Teaching English as a Foreign
 Language
Teams & Team Working
Thai
Theatre
Time Management
Tracing Your Family History
Training

Travel Writing
Trigonometry
Turkish
Turkish Conversation
Twentieth Century USA
Typing
Ukrainian
Understanding Tax for Small
 Businesses
Understanding Terrorism
Urdu
Vietnamese
Visual Basic
Volcanoes
Watercolour Painting
Weight Control through Diet &
 Exercise
Welsh
Welsh Dictionary
Welsh Grammar
Wills & Probate
Windows XP
Wine Tasting
Winning at Job Interviews
Word 2003
World Cultures: China
World Cultures: England
World Cultures: Germany
World Cultures: Italy
World Cultures: Japan
World Cultures: Portugal
World Cultures: Russia
World Cultures: Spain
World Cultures: Wales
World Faiths
Writing Crime Fiction
Writing for Children
Writing for Magazines
Writing a Novel
Writing Poetry
Xhosa
Yiddish
Yoga
Zen
Zulu